CHECK THESE "ASSISTANT ENGINEERS HANDBOOK" REVIEWS:

This book is brilliant. A major achievement. Assistant Engineers Handbook is destined to become an industry standard.
>   Simon Andrews - Owner, Right Track Studios, New York

I've done a lot of sessions with Tim, and he was always great.
>   Bob Clearmountain - Producer, Recording Engineer

Assistant Engineers Handbook is filled with the information, techniques and standards which any assistant engineer must have to make themselves indispensable. All done with a great sense of humor. Absolutely brilliant.
>   Frank Filipetti - Producer, Recording Engineer

No one is more qualified to author recording studio manuals than Tim Crich. It's a "must read" for anyone seriously considering a career in audio engineering.
>   Jim Vallance - Songwriter, Studio Owner

Full of solid information. Good job, Tim.
>   Recording Magazine

I am extremely impressed with this book. It has all the real world information that is sorely needed, but rarely (if ever) taught in engineering schools. Tim Crich has worked on tons of records including Rolling Stones, U2, KISS, Bob Dylan, Bryan Adams, even John Lennon. He has definitely been there, and he tells all.
>   Josiah Gluck - Producer, Recording Engineer

Tim Crich's wonderful book fills a much needed niche in recording literature. The common sense approach is informative and wise, while it keeps the reader chuckling. It is required reading here at Institute of Audio Research, as it should be for all aspiring recording engineers.
>   M. Friedman - Dir., Institute of Audio Research, New York

ASSISTANT ENGINEERS HANDBOOK

ASSISTANT ENGINEERS HANDBOOK

2nd EDITION

The definitive guide to working as an assistant engineer
in today's professional digital recording studio.

Written and Illustrated by Tim Crich

BLACK INK PUBLISHING
Vancouver

Black ink Publishing
Box 4295
Vancouver Canada V6B 3Z7
www.aehandbook.com
email:tcrich@intergate.ca

Assistant Engineers Handbook 2nd ed.
Library and Archives Canada Cataloguing in Publication

Crich, Tim
    Assistant engineers handbook : the definitive guide to working as an
assistant engineer in today's modern recording studio / written and
illustrated by Tim Crich.

Includes index.
ISBN 978-0-9698223-3-2

1. Sound--Recording and reproducing--Handbooks, manuals, etc.
2. Sound--Recording and reproducing--Vocational guidance. I. Title.

TK7881.4.C74 2008   621.389'3   C2008-903984-X

Printed and Bound in The United States of America

10 9 8 7 6

Copy Edited by Alison Bealy
Technical Advisor - Ron "Obvious" Vermeulen

For Melissa. There when I needed you most.

Contents at a Glance

CHAPTER ONE *Getting Started*   1
  Finding a Job   1
  Working as an Assistant Engineer   6
  Dealing With...   11

CHAPTER TWO *Setting Up the Studio*   17
  Before Starting the Setup   18
  Power in the Studio   21
  Input Setup Sheets   24
  Placing Musical Instruments   28
  Studio Equipment Setup   35

CHAPTER THREE *Cables, Microphones and Levels*   41
  Levels   41
  Cables   47
  Impedance   50
  Ground   52
  Microphone Input Panels   52
  Direct Input Boxes   54
  Running Cables   56
  Connections and Placement   57
  Microphones   64
  Headphones   70

CHAPTER FOUR *Digital and Analog Machines*   75
  Digital Audio Workstation   76
  Digital Open Reel   80
  Analog Mix Machine   81
  Alignments   84

CHAPTER FIVE *Outboard and Speakers*   96
  Outboard Equipment   96
  Placement and Connection   98
  Testing Signal Flow   101
  Studio Tie Lines   102
  Click Generators   103
  Video   104
  Speakers   104
  Analyzation And Equalization   109

CHAPTER SIX *Console and Patchbay*   110
  Normals   111
  The Console   113
  The Patchbay   118
  Chasing, Tracing and Replacing   121

CHAPTER SEVEN *Session Priorities*   125
  Priorities   125
  Getting Technical   135

CHAPTER EIGHT *Recording Basic Tracks* — 144
Media Retrieval — 144
Making Changes — 145
Changing Microphones — 146
Changing Cables — 147
Changing Headphones — 148
Changing Patches — 149
Recording Basic Tracks — 151
Tracksheets — 161
Takesheets — 161
Open Reel Labels — 163
Cues — 166

CHAPTER NINE *After Basic Tracks* — 169
Edits — 170
Repairs — 172
Recording Basic Tracks for Another Song — 164
Instrument Setup Sheets — 173
Closing the DAW Session — 177
Recording Basics for Another Song — 179
Assembling Master Multitrack Reels — 180

CHAPTER TEN *Recording Overdubs* — 184
Finding the Song — 184
Setting Up the Studio — 186
Setting Up the Console — 188
Setting Up a Previous Sound — 192
Recording — 194
Bouncing and Comping — 197
Slave Sessions — 199

CHAPTER ELEVEN *Mixdown* — 203
Final Mixes — 205
As the Mix Begins — 210
During the Mix — 214
Printing the Mix — 214
Editing the Mix — 219
Copies — 223
After the Mix — 225
Breaking Down the Mix — 233
Setting up a Remix — 234
Final Assembly — 235
Mastering — 236

CHAPTER TWELVE *After the Session* — 237
The Client — 237
Contol Room — 246
Studio — 247
Learning, the Old Fashioned Way — 252
Engineering — 253

TABLE OF CONTENTS
. . . .

ASSISTANT ENGINEERS HANDBOOK—SECOND EDITION

Contents at a Glance	viii
List of Illustrations	xxii
Acknowledgements	xxiii
Any Idiot Can Get Good Sound	xxiv

CHAPTER ONE *Getting Started* — 1

FINDING A JOB — 1
Schools	1
Résumés	3
Experience	4
Starting as a Runner	4

WORKING AS AN ASSISTANT ENGINEER — 6
Hours and Wages	6
Duties	7
Attitude	8

DEALING WITH... — 11
Recording Engineers	11
Record Producers	12
Clients and Artists	13
Studio Managers	15

CHAPTER TWO *Setting Up the Studio*   17

BEFORE STARTING THE SETUP   18
Supplies   18
Environments in the Rooms   20

POWER IN THE STUDIO   21
AC Cables   21
Power Transformers   21
Grounding   22
Batteries   23
Power Up   23

INPUT/SETUP SHEETS   24

PLACING MUSICAL INSTRUMENTS   28
Road Cases   28
Drums   29
Amplifiers   30
Bass Amplifier   31
Guitar 1 Amplifier   31
Guitar 2 Amplifier   31
Piano   32
Organs   32
Electronic Keyboards   33
Additional Instruments   33
Tuners   33

STUDIO EQUIPMENT SETUP   35
Baffles   35
Chairs   38
Microphone Stands   38

CHAPTER THREE *Cables, Microphones and Levels*   41

LEVELS   41
Signal Processing   41
The Decibel   43
Levels   44
Digital/Analog Distortion   46
The Sound Envelope   46

CABLES   47
Balanced Cables   47
Unbalanced Cables   48
MIDI Cable   49

IMPEDANCE   50

GROUND   52

MICROPHONE INPUT PANELS   52

DIRECT INPUT BOXES   54
Effects Boxes   55

RUNNING CABLES   56
Bringing Cables   56

CONNECTIONS AND PLACEMENT   57

MICROPHONES   64
Retrieving Microphones   65
Connection Mounts   66

Microphone Placement 67
Pop Filters 69
Room Microphones 70

HEADPHONES 70
Headphone Boxes 71
Cue Options 71
Headphones for the Players 72
Headphones for the Engineer 73
Headphones for the Assistant 73

CHAPTER FOUR *Digital and Analog Machines* 75

Digital Connections 76
Setup Sheet 76

DIGITAL AUDIO WORKSTATION 76
Create a Master 76

DIGITAL OPEN REEL 80

ANALOG MIX MACHINE 81
Analog Connections 81
Front of the Machine 81
Cleaning 82
Demagnetizing 83
Heads, Tails and Pre-Print Through 84

ALIGNMENTS 84
Levels 84
Load the Tone Reel 86
Playback Alignment 87

Contents

Removing a Reel/Packing 89
Record Alignment 60
Loading and Exercising 90
Oscillator 91
Bias 91
Recording Tones 92
Create a Tone Reel 93
After the Alignment 94
Check Each Reel 94

CHAPTER FIVE *Outboard and Speakers* 96

OUTBOARD EQUIPMENT 96
Standard Outboard Racks 97
Additional Outboard 97
Renting Equipment 98

PLACEMENT AND CONNECTION 98
Power Up/Power Down 99
Back Panel 100
Connections 100

TESTING SIGNAL FLOW 101
Unity Gain 101
Reset 102

STUDIO TIE LINES 102

CLICK GENERATORS 103

VIDEO 104

SPEAKERS   104
Speaker Removal and Replacement   105
Additional Speakers   107
Speakers for Cue   107

ANALYZATION AND EQUALIZATION   109

CHAPTER SIX Console and Patchbay   110

NORMALS   111
Breaking the Normals   112

THE CONSOLE   113
Zeroing the Console   113
Labelling the Scribble Strip   113
Digital Scribble Strip   115
Console Status Mode   116
Bussing   116

THE PATCHBAY   118
Microphone Inputs   120
Line Inputs   121

CHASING, TRACING AND REPLACING   121
Cue Sends   122
Master Sends and Returns   123
Talkback   123

CHAPTER SEVEN Session Priorities   125

PRIORITIES   125
Telephone Protocol   130

The Door   131
When the Company Rep Stops By   131
Coffee and Tea   132
Ordering Out   132
Eating your Lunch   133
Down Time   134
When Things Go Wrong   135

GETTING TECHNICAL   135
Technical Staff   135
The Shop   136
Maintenance Forms   137
Daily Log   139
Inventory Sheets   141
Mistakes   142

CHAPTER EIGHT *Recording Basic Tracks*   144

MEDIA RETRIEVAL   144

MAKING CHANGES   145

CHANGING MICROPHONES   146
Changing Microphone Parameters   147
Final Microphone Placement   147

CHANGING CABLES   147

CHANGING HEADPHONES   148

CHANGING PATCHES   149

RECORDING BASIC TRACKS   151
Running the Recorder   152

TRACKSHEETS 154
Project Information 154
DAW Tracksheet/Recording Map 155
Open Reel Tracksheet 157

TAKESHEETS 161
Project Information 161
Titles and Locations 161

OPEN REEL LABELS 163
Titles and Locations 165
Spine 165
Labelling the Reel 166

CUES 166
Progress Chart 167

CHAPTER NINE *After Basic Tracks* 169

EDITS 170

REPAIRS 172
Musician in the Studio 172
Musician in the Control Room 172

INSTRUMENT SETUP SHEETS 173
Creating and Documenting 173

CLOSING THE DAW SESSION 177
File Management 178
Labelling 179

RECORDING BASICS FOR ANOTHER SONG 179

ASSEMBLING MASTER REELS 180
Labelling 183

CHAPTER TEN *Recording Overdubs*   184

   FINDING THE SONG   184

   SETTING UP THE STUDIO   186

   SETTING UP THE CONSOLE   188
   Console Status   188
   Signal Routing   188
   Testing the Inputs   190
   Rest of the Console   191

   SETTING UP A PREVIOUS SOUND   192
   Monitor Mix   193
   Cue Mix   194

   RECORDING   194
   Punching In and Out   194
   Changing Tracks   196

   BOUNCING AND COMPING   197
   Comping Tracks on the Open Reel   197
   Comping Tracks on the DAW   198
   Vocal Tuning   199

   SLAVE SESSIONS   199
   Outgoing   199
   Returning Data   201

CHAPTER ELEVEN *Mixdown*   203

   Rough Mixes   204

FINAL MIXES   205

Control Room   205
Console   206
Digital Audio Workstation   207
Analog Mix Machine   208
DAT Recorders   209
CD Burners   210

AS THE MIX BEGINS   210

Patching   211
Crosspatching   211
Additional Patching   212

DURING THE MIX   214

PRINTING THE MIX   214

Input Levels   215
Open Reel   215
DAT Cassette Machine   217
CD Burner   218
Disc/DAT Labelling   218

EDITING THE MIX   219

Tape Edits   220
During the Edits   222
Undoing a Tape Edit   223
Practicing Your Edits   223

COPIES   223

The Copy Room   224
Your Personal Collection   225

AFTER THE MIX	225
Documenting the Mix	225
Mix Setup Sheets	226
Session Information	226
Patching	227
Outboard Equipment	228
Setup Sheet Storage	233
BREAKING DOWN THE MIX	233
SETTING UP A RE-MIX	234
FINAL ASSEMBLY	235
Labelling the Final Mix Reel	235
MASTERING	236
CHAPTER TWELVE *After the Session*	237
THE CLIENT	237
Work Order	237
Payment	240
SESSION BREAKDOWN	241
Labelling and File Organization	241
Disc Storage	241
Tapes	242
Vault/Control Numbers	242
MEDIA CONTROL	243
Outgoing Media	243
Transporting Tapes/Media	245

CONTROL ROOM   246

STUDIO   247

Cables   249
Microphones   250
Headphones, Tuners, Direct Boxes   250
Instruments   251
The Rest of the Room   251
The Next Session   252

LEARNING, THE OLD FASHIONED WAY   252

ENGINEERING   253
The Ladder   254
The Big Break   254
Record Credits and You   255
Stay in Contact   255
Final Notes   256

Blank Studio Forms   258
Index   269

LIST OF ILLUSTRATIONS

. . . .

2.1	Power Transformer	21
2.2	Ground Lifter	22
2.3	Input/Setup Sheet	26
2.4	Back of Input Sheet	27
2.5	Baffles	36
2.6	Isolation Booth	37
3.1	Breakdown of Device	42
3.2	SPL vs. Decibel	44
3.3	Levels	45
3.4	Sound Envelope	46
3.5	Balanced Cable	47
3.6	Unbalanced Cables	48
3.7	Impedance Differences	50
3.8	Microphone Panel	53
3.9	Direct Box	55
3.10	Cable Extension	60
3.11	Microphone Pad	62
3.12	Quick Connectors	66
3.13	Pop Filters	69
3.14	Headphone Box	71
4.1	Session Sheet	77
4.2	NanoWebers/VU	85
5.1	Outboard Rack	97
5.2	Speaker Triangle	106
5.3	Speaker Cue Setup	108
6.1	Patchbay Normals	111
6.2	Normals	112
6.3	Scribble Strip	114
7.1	Maintenance Form	138
7.2	Daily Log	140
7.3	Inventory Sheet	141
8.1	DAW Tracksheet	156
8.2	Open Reel Tracksheet	158
8.3	Takesheet/Map	162
8.4	Tape Label	164
8.5	Labelling The Reel	166
8.6	Progress Chart	167
9.1	Setup Sheet	175
9.2	Outboard Setup	177
9.3	Master Tape Label	182
11.1	Delay Chart	213
11.2	Session Information	229
11.3	Patching	230
11.4	Sends And Returns	231
11.5	Outboard Equipment	232
12.1	Work Order	238
12.2	Media Control Form	244
12.3	Winding a Cable	248
	Digital Reel Label	258
	Takesheet/Map	259
	Tracksheet	260
	DAW Tracksheet	262
	Maintenance Report	263
	Session Sheet	264
	Mixdown Log Sheet	265
	Media Control	266
	Work Order	267
	Inventory	268

ACKNOWLEDGEMENTS

. . . .

Grateful acknowledgement and a special thank you to the following:

Bryan Adams, Bob Clearmountain, Jon Bon Jovi, Gene Simmons,
Ron Obvious, Bob Rock, Bruce Fairbairn, Rick Eden, Paul McGrath,
Bob Schwall, Tim King, Alan Friedman, Mark Hermann, Paul Hamingson,
Simon Andrews, Frank Filipetti, Moira Marquis, Josiah Gluck, Noah Baron,
Michael Brauer, Noel Smith, Kevin Williams, Glenn Crich, Joan Crich,
Matthew Crich, Buck Crich.

ANY IDIOT CAN GET GOOD SOUND

. . . .

Any idiot can get good sound. This is a statement that was told to me by a great recording engineer (who shall remain nameless) while I was his assistant engineer on an equally great record (which will also remain nameless). While any idiot can get good sound, any idiot cannot be a great recording engineer. It takes hard work, dedication, talent, skill, luck and massive amounts of caffeine.

It can be a long journey to becoming a recording engineer—you usually have to start at the bottom and work your way up. A good deal of the time will probably be spent working as an assistant engineer.

Working as an assistant engineer is a wonderful job. You listen to great music all day, hang out with famous people, and work in an environment that looks like NASA's Mission Control. It's a knob twirler's delight. You get your name on lots of records, you get free concert tickets with backstage passes, and sometimes you get free meals. You even get paid—not much, but you do get paid.

Until now, there has been no manual, no guide, no handbook for the aspiring assistant engineer. This book is a compilation of notes, ideas and observations from my years as staff assistant engineer at the prestigious Right Track Recording Studios in New York City, and the legendary Little Mountain Sound Studios in Vancouver, Canada. In these studios, and others, I worked on thousands of sessions, including some of the most successful recordings of all time.

If you want to be a recording engineer, you have taken a major step by opening this book. This is the ultimate guide for any newcomer who is serious about advancing in this very lucrative and satisfying field.

There are many fine books available that explain the technical operations of recording studios. This is not one of them. This book is a practical, hands-on guide to help the assistant engineer with his or her daily duties in a recording studio. It's more like a driver's guide than an engine manual, therefore explanations of how the equipment operates are not included. To learn more about the technical aspects of recording studios, I urge you to read as many up-to-date books, magazine articles, and internet resources about the technical end of recording studios as you can get your hands on. You must have this knowledge to do your job properly.

Throughout this book I refer to the worker in the studio as "he" simply because it is awkward to say "he/she" all the time. I feel that anyone, male or female should have the same opportunities to rise through the ranks of the recording studio. To the vast majority of studio owners, producers and engineers, gender is not an issue. The only issue is the ability to do the job. Now let's get to the good stuff!

Tim Crich

CHAPTER ONE
. . . .

Getting Started

Welcome to *Assistant Engineers Handbook*—the only book available written especially for the assistant recording engineer. Every song on every disc in every music store across the land was made possible by a recording engineer who was once a beginner, and every beginner needs a job.

FINDING A JOB

A diploma or degree from a recognized recording school, a good résumé, and experience go a long way to helping you find a job in a recording studio. It's not like the old days when you hung around outside a studio until they finally asked you to come in and help with the engineering. With the high competition for jobs you have to show the people doing the hiring that you are serious about becoming a recording engineer. But don't despair. The increasing number of digital home and professional studios is producing a greater demand for qualified people.

SCHOOLS

Working in a recording studio is the best way to learn, but most people starting out simply don't get that opportunity. Schools are a great place to start in the recording industry because they offer beginners exposure to the basics of audio engineering, recording studio operations, and access to local musicians, recording engineers and producers.

Many fine schools offer recording engineer classes. Some also offer courses in studio maintenance, artist management, record production, video post production, and a host of additional subjects covering almost all aspects of the music industry; some even offer classes on both résumé preparation and interview techniques. Some schools are affiliated with local studios and offer an internship program after graduation. Some offer cheap or free studio time to local bands for the students to practice their recording skills.

First, decide what your goals are, how long you want to attend school, and how much tuition you can afford. Then research the curriculum of the available schools.

Ask these questions:

- What level of education is required? Do you need a high school diploma or equivalency before being accepted?

- Does the school offer financial aid? Many schools offer help to students through government grants and loans.

- Are there on-site facilities, or does the school book time at a local studio for classes? Your tuition should go toward your education, not to a studio whose primary objective is profit. A school with an in-house recording studio will offer more hands-on experience.

- Have the instructors spent much time in a studio, or do they have limited experience? Teachers with studio experience are always preferable.

- Do you get transferable college credits for graduating?

- Does the school have a placement program? Some schools try to help new graduates find work in local studios.

- Will the school provide names of graduates you may contact? If so, speak to the graduates and find out if they were satisfied with the school's curriculum, the placement process, and any follow-up programs.

- Does the curriculum fit your needs? A six-week course cannot give you all the studio electronics, sound theory and musical instruction that a four-year program can. If you are interested in engineering, you shouldn't have to take any unrelated courses, such as managing bands.

Graduating from a recording school does not guarantee employment. Rarely does a studio hire engineers with no engineering experience, and it is unrealistic to expect a studio to hire you as an engineer just because you have a diploma. No matter how much schooling you have, you will still probably start at the bottom as a studio runner. It doesn't take four years of schooling to learn how to make a fresh pot of coffee, but if making the coffee gets you into a recording studio, do it.

Schools can be great places to meet people and make connections, but they can't do it all. Sitting in a classroom and working in a studio are two entirely different things. In school, if you make a mistake, it's "No, this is how it's done." In the studio, it's "You erased the WHAT?"

RESUMES

Studios receive many résumés—make sure that the one they get from you looks professional. Go through the Yellow Pages and make a list of all eligible recording studios. Before sending your résumé, telephone the studio to find out the name and title of the person doing the hiring (be sure to get the correct spelling), and the name of the person you are speaking to. Mention the telephone contact in the cover letter, such as "I spoke to 'so and so' on this date, and she recommended that I send you a résumé." If you speak with the person who does the hiring, so much the better.

Send them two typed pages; a cover letter, and a biography. Make sure they are clearly written and neatly presented, and stress experience over schooling. Chances of getting a job are better if you have some experience behind an audio console. Follow up the résumé with a phone call to the same person. "I spoke to you on this date, and you told me to send a résumé. I just want to make sure you received it?"

Keep track of where, when, and to whom you sent all résumés, and what was said during the follow-up calls. Be persistent and don't take "no" for an answer. Send updated résumés and keep calling until somebody hires you.

EXPERIENCE

While applying at the local studios, try to find work in any possible audio situation. With the abundance of local bands and clubs, you should be able to find work, even if it's doing live sound for a friend's band. Many musicians own a ton of recording gear, with little knowledge of how to use it, and they need someone who can run everything. Get your name out there, and find work any way you can.

Go to industry trade shows, subscribe to the magazines, and attend equipment workshops sponsored by professional audio dealers. The more you know about the studio system and its workings, the better your chances of rising through the ranks. As in any business, you keep up or you get left behind.

STARTING AS A RUNNER

Recording studios commonly hire people with little or no experience as runners (also called interns or apprentices). Runners are the beginners in the studio, hired to do the menial chores such as running to the deli, the stationery store, the post office, or other recording studios.

As a runner, you will also be a telephone operator, a doorman, a housekeeper, a receptionist, a delivery person, a waiter, a whipping post, and a host of other exciting career opportunities. The only real time spent in the recording rooms is when bringing in equipment or food, or when helping the assistant with setup or breakdown. Runners often work long hours for very little or no pay, and are there primarily for the learning experience. This is a difficult concept for some people to understand, especially your parents.

Many of today's top engineers started out as runners. There are very few engineers who skipped the technical training and internship, and began as engineers. Typically you must work as a runner, then as an assistant before sitting in the engineer's chair.

Some people often spend years working as a runner, expecting to get promoted, when they don't actually understand what is involved with the job. A lot of people not really suited to the job drop out during this difficult period, not realizing the dedication required.

The only way for a runner to learn is to hang out in sessions. During slow times in the day, and after checking with the engineer or assistant, go into the control room and quietly sit in a corner, This is where you absorb all the information possible. Talking, laughing and joking with the client out in the lobby is fine, but in the control room, keep quiet. If you don't understand something, ask the session assistant when appropriate, such as after the session.

If you're good, you might occasionally work as assistant when the assistant works as the engineer on low budget or house projects. Some studios strike a deal with an unsigned band by offering free studio time during off hours, with the studio reaping a share of any profits gained from record sales. This is called a house project.

When you prove you can do the job, you may get promoted. You may even start to get paid. The smaller the studio, the sooner you can expect to be promoted to assistant engineer. In a major studio, it may take longer, but with perseverance, you will eventually be bringing coffee to first rate engineers and producers.

WORKING AS AN ASSISTANT ENGINEER

Somewhere between sweeping floors and sweeping equalization is the position of assistant engineer. The engineer is concentrating on getting the best sounds he can. The producer is concentrating on the music, the parts, and the arrangements. The band is concentrating on playing well. That leaves everything else up to the assistant engineer—you.

This is a job where the work is demanding. You really must know that this is the business for you or you simply won't last. Once you become an engineer, you can expect to make a good living. But working your way up the recording studio ladder can be a difficult process. For years I was on the "New York City Recording Studio Diet" which consisted of three parts:

1) Walking 43 blocks to work every day.

2) Eating once every two or three days, whether I needed to or not.

3) Running 43 blocks home as fast as I possibly could in the middle of the night.

You must be very dedicated to the idea that one day you will be sitting in the engineer's chair.

HOURS AND WAGES

Long hours for the assistant engineer are legendary. Sessions are long enough as it is, but the assistant arrives earlier, and leaves later than anyone else in the session. As well as long hours, there is usually no such thing as a weekend off—or making plans for next Friday night. Marathon weekend sessions are routine. In most jobs, after a regular shift is finished, a worker is relieved by another worker. Not so in the recording studio. Usually an assistant is assigned to a project, and stays with it no matter how many hours are involved.

The concept of day and night falls into some vast unknown void. When I was assistant engineer on the Rolling Stones' "Dirty Work" it was not unusual to arrive at the studio around midnight. By 3 or 4 a.m. Keith Richards would stagger in, and the session would begin.

You can forget about having any sort of romantic relationship. The only people who really understand the commitment to these long hours are other people in the recording industry. And who wants to hang out with them?

The wages for assistant engineers tend to be quite low. So low that the bowl of fruit and pastries provided by the studio for the clients was often my only daily sustenance. The studio manager once said "I never thought of Keith Richards as the sort of guy to eat a complete bowl of fruit every day!" Little did he know.

DUTIES

Your job is to do everything required to keep the session rolling along smoothly from before everyone arrives, until after everyone leaves. You will do all the little things so the rest of the session staff can concentrate on the music. Due to a lack of standardization from studio to studio, your duties may vary. In one studio, you may do all the machine alignments; in another, you may answer the phones and do all the bookings. A good assistant can greatly speed up the recording process. A bad assistant can bring it to a screeching halt. Overall the duties of the assistant include—

- Transporting all tapes, discs, and hard drives between the vault and the control room, changing tapes throughout the session, and operating and maintaining all recording machines.

- Setting up and breaking down all audio, musical and electronic equipment necessary for the session.

- Making all equipment changes, such as cables, patchcords, outboard equipment and microphones.

- Keeping track of the paperwork, including tracksheets, takesheets, labels, work orders, maintenance forms, notes, as well as a log of daily events.

- Keeping track of and labelling all audio workstation files and sessions.

- Helping everyone with any equipment setup or session needs.

- Making the engineer look good in front of the client.

- Keeping the rooms clean, stocked, organized and comfortable.

- Doing the best job possible to keep the recording session running smoothly and on schedule.

ATTITUDE

Even if you do all the above, it still may not be enough. To get ahead in the session you must gain the confidence of the players, the engineer and the producer by being—

- Agreeable. No matter how well you do the job, no one will want to work with you if you have a bad attitude. Being agreeable is not always an easy task when you spend hour after hour, day after day in the studio with the same people. Do the best job you can, even when you are dead tired and facing another long day tomorrow. With a good positive attitude, the rest comes easy. Enthusiasm, confidence and professionalism will be recognized and appreciated. You should be good natured, but not to the point where the session is a joke. Taking a sincere interest in the outcome of the project just comes naturally.

    If you change employment from one studio to another, learn how the new studio operates, and do everything their way. Every studio operates differently, and each feels their way is the right way. Don't come in and tell them that they are doing this or that wrong. They mean it when they say "This is the way we've always done it, and it works for us." Every assistant can learn different methods.

• Knowledgeable. Understand everything about the equipment in the studio, including correct setup, use, and breakdown. Engineers rely heavily on the assistants to help them grasp unfamiliar equipment or computer editing programs and software. Without understanding the workings of every piece of equipment in the studio, you can't effectively assist the engineer.

• A hard worker. You need to go the extra mile to be remembered. Give the extra touch to the session and make the engineer feel that he is respected. If you load the machine and walk away, that may be fine for most engineers. Better yet, load the machine, find the correct spot on the reel, set up the console, re-write the scribble strip, do the patching, and get the engineer a soda. Chances are, you will be remembered and requested for future sessions—maybe even recommended to other engineers as a good assistant. As in any job, you must apply yourself to get ahead.

• Organized. Keep the rooms comfortable, clean, and well organized, with everything you may need at your fingertips. Look organized, even if it is difficult to be organized. Put away all the unused equipment. Everything has a home, keep it there. Toss all used paper cups, food wrappers and soda cans.

Erase pencil marks and smudges off the equipment, except any settings marked, such as a favorite level. Keep all the papers and lyrics in order. You may not be totally organized, but the client should think you are. When the rooms are disorganized and untidy, people naturally become anxious. The more comfortable the rooms are, the better the atmosphere, and ultimately, the better the outcome of the project.

- Reliable. This is not a job where you can call in sick whenever you want. You are the person who runs the session, and without you there may be no session. During a large project, if the assistant is regularly late or absent he will be replaced with someone more reliable. However, there are exceptions. During the recording of Bryan Adams' "Waking up the Neighbours" I was stricken with a kidney stone, and had to leave the session early. When I returned the next day, the band had recorded a version of that classic Bob Dylan song, "Like a Kidney Stone."

- Well read. Read as many books and magazines about the recording industry as possible. The more you know about the studio and its technologies, the better you will be equipped to do your job. Being well read gives you credibility. If a client or engineer asks your opinion of the new "triple turbo super digital tube modulator," you should have at least a basic knowledge of its workings.

- Musical. Most clients would prefer to work with an engineering staff that has a musical background. After all, this is the music business. If you don't own a musical instrument, get one and learn the basics, at least enough to recognize chords and notes when you see or hear them being played. Knowing how to play a musical instrument gets you a sense of tuning, a sense of timing, and plenty of dates.

- Discreet. Sometimes you will be involved in the session, helping with suggestions and ideas, and sometimes you simply blend into the woodwork. A good assistant is like a good waiter at a fine restaurant. He is not always noticed, but everything is quietly taken care of. Discretion dictates when and when not to be noticed.

- Positive. Keep the vibe of the session up. Clients want to feel that the engineer is in complete control. If you are working with an engineer who has made a mistake in the past, don't bring that up. If clients hear how he erased something on a different project, they will not have full confidence in him. They want to concentrate totally on the music, not on whether the engineer is going to accidentally erase something. Make them feel that they are getting a reliable studio and staff.

Think before speaking. What may be a revelation to you may be obvious to an experienced engineer. Don't start adding your little ideas or offerings to the session unless you are absolutely positively sure you have something beneficial to contribute.

Don't badmouth your studio, your co-workers or any engineers. The recording community is surprisingly small, and these things can return to haunt you.

• Hygienic. You will be stuck in a small room, for hours upon hours, working closely with your colleagues. When you are in a marathon session, every once in a while take a quick break to refresh yourself by splashing your face with water. Carry a toothbrush, and use it. You will look better, fell better and smell better. Not wearing a clean shirt may be the fad this week, but it doesn't encourage clients to return to your studio. As we all know, it can be uncomfortable to be stuck working next to a person who doesn't realize he has an odor problem.

DEALING WITH...

Being an assistant engineer involves not only working with electronic equipment, but also dealing with people.

RECORDING ENGINEERS

Most recording engineers work in various recording studios, and with many different assistant engineers. If the engineer likes you and the way you work, he may want to use you on all of his sessions. With a good rapport between you and the engineer, your sessions should be smooth and trouble free.

The only way to do the best job possible is to learn from all the engineers you work with. Most engineers are happy to show the eager assistant why they use, for example, a certain delay, or favorite special effect. If you get on well with the engineer, you can ask him questions about his methods of recording that you might not feel comfortable asking other engineers.

To do your job, you must learn as much as possible about different methods of recording. Each engineer has different tricks and ways of doing things, and each feels that his way is correct. Write down any new methods or techniques of recording used by different engineers. This will be very helpful when you start engineering. However, don't divulge one engineer's secrets to another. Just use them yourself.

If you like a certain engineer and how he works, you might want to request working with him on all his sessions at your studio. Clear this with him and with the studio manager. Unless the engineer really doesn't like you, this should not be a problem.

The best way to work with your favorite engineer is to do such a great job that he requests you whenever he works at your studio. If you always do a good job, he may give you a certain degree of freedom, such as editing, setting an equalization, or perhaps even a bit of engineering.

Another good reason to get to know an engineer and do a good job for him is that if he gets into production, he will be looking for an engineer to fill his position. This is a perfect opportunity for you, because he knows you, knows how you work, and knows that you do a good job. This is called getting ahead in the recording industry.

RECORD PRODUCERS

The definition of a record producer is certainly vague. He is usually the person responsible for the final product. Some producers take care of all financial dealings, including equipment rentals, musician fees, studio costs, etc. Some will also help write the songs, do the arrangements, play the instruments, and do all the engineering. A good producer realizes each musician, project and session needs to be approached differently. Methods of getting the best performance out of one artist may not work with another. He also knows when to push the artist a bit more, when he has the best performance recorded, when it's time to move on, and when to tell the difference.

Most of today's more popular producers are very patient and talented people who do a good job and deserve their success. However, there is the occasional producer who spends all day on the telephone, occasionally interrupting his conversation to say to the band, "Yeah, sounds great, you guys are gonna be stars. Any sushi left?"

Producers, being in charge of the project, have been known to take advantage of the lowly assistant engineer, like having him pick up the dry cleaning or wash the car, or even shaving some time off the studio bill. You work harder than anyone else in the session, so do not let them take advantage of you. Of course, giving them an extra fifteen minutes occasionally, just enough to endear yourself to them, may not hurt.

Don't argue with the producer. He has the highest priority in the studio. Try to get along with him, no matter how difficult or unreasonable he may be. Of course, if he wants to record the sound of the control room window smashing for the band's next hit single, you might want to step in and discuss it with him.

CLIENTS AND ARTISTS

The clients are the reason you have a job. They are paying the bills, so ultimately they are the ones who must be satisfied. I once worked with a singer who was unhappy singing into the small microphone that the engineer preferred. He felt he was so talented he needed a large microphone, not a wimpy little one. The engineer realized that since the singer was paying the bills he was the boss. The engineer had me change microphones from the high quality smaller microphone to a larger, albeit lower quality, microphone. That lesson taught me that the client is always right.

The clients, however, aren't always the musicians. With jingles, for example, they might be an advertising agency; for a record project, they might be the record company; for a demo, they might be the musicians. Everyone involved in the session besides the engineering staff is commonly referred to as the client. Whoever the clients are, they are using your studio because they want predictable results. The assistant is usually provided by the studio to assure that the clients get what they want.

From the time they arrive to the time they leave, the clients should be comfortable and happy. This means that you show them their location in the studio and help them with their instruments. They will need help with anything and everything that needs to be set up, plugged in, taped, wired, adjusted, added, removed, or simply twiddled with. Make the clients feel that the studio staff involved in their project are very qualified.

Throughout the session, if anyone is having any problems at all, go out and help. If a musician removes his headphones to change or adjust them, or if he begins to change the microphone stand, go out and make the change. He is not there to fix or adjust anything—this is your job. When he sees you coming out to help, the next time he wants something changed, rather than doing it himself, he will just call you. Your goal is to make the clients feel comfortable enough to want to return to your studio for future projects.

Here are a few guidelines for dealing with clients:

• Don't stop musicians when they are in the middle of playing. It is not your place. Musicians tend to get "in the groove" while playing, and they might not appreciate being interrupted by the lowly assistant. Leave that to the engineer or producer.

• Avoid singing your own little versions of the songs you are working on. Imagine how impressed George Martin would have been had he heard the assistant engineer singing "All You Need Is Lunch."

• Be especially careful when joking with clients. Most sessions seem casual, but a lot of money, time, and hard work is involved. Jokes about erasing a track, or not being in *record* during a great take are not funny. It can be disheartening to the musicians if, after a great take, the assistant jokingly says, "Oh, I guess we should have recorded that, nyuk, nyuk." It may seem hilarious to you, but it shows your studio inexperience.

• Don't mention how much their song reminds you of another song. Every songwriter likes to feel his work is somewhat original, not a re-hash of someone else's music.

- Don't say "Man, that really stinks." A good assistant engineer must be diplomatic. If they ask for your opinion, tell them the truth, and you will earn more respect in the long term. Be positive, even if it's "Hey, I really dig that high-hat." If you don't have an opinion, get one.

- Befriend the clients. If they like you and the way you work, they may want to return to your studio for their next project—perhaps even use you to engineer.

- Represent the studio responsibly. Sometimes your job pits you between management and clients. The clients may take their frustrations with the studio out on you, and management at times gets on you for the client's behavior in the studio. When it comes right down to it, a good studio will side with the staff.

- Be absolutely quiet when arguments arise—and they will. Being in a small room for great lengths of time can create friction between people. It is not your place to step in and try to ease the situation unless the actual studio is threatened. If the situation comes to blows then, as always, punch the littlest guy.

STUDIO MANAGERS

The studio manager is generally the person who books the studio, does the hiring and firing, and keeps the whole place in order. He may be an owner, an engineer, both, or neither. The manager is linked to the studio by the assistant engineers, and can only run a studio well if he knows what is going on within the actual sessions. Give him clear legible paperwork, and keep him informed of tape or equipment used, down time or schedule changes. He shouldn't be the last to know the project being worked on is going to run over schedule.

Keep the manager happy. If he isn't happy with the way you work, you may not be working on the best projects that come in. There really isn't anything wrong with working on the next "Polka Pals 'n Gals" record, but you probably want to do projects with a little more exposure.

15

. . . .

Summary

Chapter One explained how to get started in the recording industry:

- How to prepare for getting a job in the recording studio, including résumé preparation, looking for a job and applying at different recording studios.

- What is involved in being a runner.

- What is expected of a good assistant engineer; including the dedication needed, the hours and wages, the duties, and the right attitude.

- How to deal with the people in the recording studio, including recording engineers, producers, clients and musicians, and studio managers.

2

CHAPTER TWO

. . . .

Setting up the Studio

Recording studios do much more than record the songs we hear on the radio. The spoken word, sound effects, jingles, videos, video games, film and television soundtracks, even cellphone ring tones are very much a part of today's recording industry. Although this book mainly applies to sessions involving musical instruments, it can be adapted to any specific application not directly related to music. References to the musician may be adapted to any non-music related artists, such as voice-over announcers.

Methods of setup and recording vary widely from engineer to engineer and from studio to studio, so it is not possible to detail all situations you may encounter. Some recording studios leave the musical instruments set up, so breakdown isn't required after each session. Other studios have house instruments such as drums, pianos, guitars and amplifiers that are used for every session. Some studios are strictly digital, using instruments and recording methods that are completely within the digital realm.

Basic tracks, simply called basics, or beds, are the first, or primary instruments to be recorded. (See Chapter Eight for more on basics.) Overdubs are then dubbed over, or recorded along with the basics to finish with a final complete passage of music. (See Chapter Ten for more on overdubs.) Whether doing basics or overdubs, setting up the instruments is generally the same. The only differences are placement of the musical instrument or musician, and the amount of setup time required. Setup for a large or complex basic session may take up to a few hours, while setup for an overdub session should take no longer than an hour. Instruments tend to be set up and recorded individually for overdubs.

Note that the term recording studio usually covers the complete building, or floor, or business. When referring to the individual rooms, usually the studio is where the musicians play the music, the control room is where the engineer records it, and the bathroom is where the musicians pass out.

BEFORE STARTING THE SETUP

Check the scheduled start time, and judge when to arrive to begin setting up. Leave a little more time than you think you need in case the setup takes longer than planned. For a larger session, try to bring in a runner to help set up and check the equipment.

When a large session is scheduled to begin in the morning, it's best to start the setup the night before, rather than arrive at some ridiculously early hour. If overdubs or mixes are taking place in the control room the night before, the studio may be available for cleaning and setting up equipment. Before going in, ask the engineer for permission, don't ask the client. Some clients may feel that they are paying for the whole recording studio, and they don't want anyone setting up for another session on their time. If the studio is not in use the night before, check with the studio manager first.

SUPPLIES

The control room and studio must be neat and tidy with all supplies organized and close at hand. You might want to have your own personal collection of some of the following smaller items, including—

- Pens, pencils, china markers or grease pencils (various colors), Sharpie felt pens (various colors), and pads of writing paper. Engineers seem to have this thing about sharp pencils, so place at least one pencil on or near the console.

- Unused paperwork, such as blank tracksheets, takesheets, maintenance forms, plus enough tape and disc labels. You should never have to hunt around for any important forms in the middle of a session. A three-hole punch keeps all paperwork organized in the daily log. (See Chapter Seven for more on the daily log.)

- A comfortable area for the workstation, with headphones or speakers, depending on the situation. Turn all computer equipment on and open applicable files. If necessary, the client may have the files on a hard drive or DVD. Copy these over to the master computer as described in Chapter Ten. As well, place a pad of paper and a sharpened pencil nearby for quick notes and numbers.

- Stock digital tapes, CDs, DVDs, hard drives or whatever storage medium the session is using. Some tapes, such as A-DATs will need formatting before use. Stock plenty of CDs, because it is common to burn a CD for everyone at the end of the session. As well, CDs and DVDs are commonly used for data storage and backup.

- Various kinds of adhesive tape. White adhesive tape is often used when writing the scribble strip on the console. (See Chapter Six for more on the scribble strip.) Avoid conventional masking tape as it leaves a sticky film wherever it is used. Place a few rolls of duct tape around the studio for anyone to grab and use. Hide a roll of duct tape away somewhere so you'll always have one in an emergency.

- Enough power. Place all electrical extension cords and boxes in a convenient place. As well, keep a supply of batteries of various voltages.

- A flashlight, in case you need to check equipment connections.

- Plenty of paper towels and tissue boxes in the control room and studio.

- Manuals for any new or rental equipment with which you or the engineer might not be familiar.

- Packing blankets, sand bags and small carpets nearby in the studio for use during setup. Set out enough ashtrays and matches for those poor souls who still smoke. Maybe bring in an air purifier.

ENVIRONMENTS IN THE ROOMS

- Sweep or vacuum the control room and studio thoroughly, empty all trash cans and replace the liners. Any equipment from other sessions, such as road cases must be put elsewhere for storage.

- Change burnt out light bulbs in the control room and studio. If applicable, replace them with the same color bulbs. Proper lighting in the studio can help when musicians are trying to be creative.

- Keep the rooms comfortably cool. Wide changes in temperature may cause some musical instruments to go out of tune. As well, understand the serious consequences of leaving the air conditioner off, or the heater on high overnight.

- If you or someone in the session feels the temperature needs adjusting, change it by a few degrees, not all the way up or all the way off. If the air conditioner cuts out, the excessive heat in the control room can cause the internal workings of some expensive studio equipment to go into near thermo-nuclear meltdown, losing all settings and custom programs.

  Because different people have different views on ideal temperature, clients love to turn the thermostat up or down. They turn it up as if it is the volume control on the final listen back. If you feel even the slightest temperature change, check to see if the thermostat is set properly.

- Eliminate squeaks. All door hinges must be quiet. Entry into the control room and studio should be silent, not squeaky. Sometimes people like to enter and leave without being heard.

POWER IN THE STUDIO

AC CABLES

Of course, all equipment in the studio needs power. Whenever placing equipment, always use its original power cord. Perhaps even label the cord with the name and number of the corresponding equipment.

Often studios simply don't have enough outlets to house all the power cords from the various equipment in the studio. Quad boxes, or power strips, are heavy duty extension cords with four receptacles at one end, and a single plug at the other. With these strategically placed throughout the studio, most equipment will be close to an available power source.

POWER TRANSFORMERS

Transformers step the power down from the wall outlet to an acceptable voltage level required for some equipment. A coil of wires is wrapped around an iron core with a specific number of coils, or turns. This coil is housed next to a second coil of wires wrapped around this same core with a different number of coils. These "coil ratios" determine the voltage and impedance levels that transfer from one coil to the other. Guitar pedals, effects, keyboards, and other recording equipment that operate on batteries usually come with transformers (Figure 2.1).

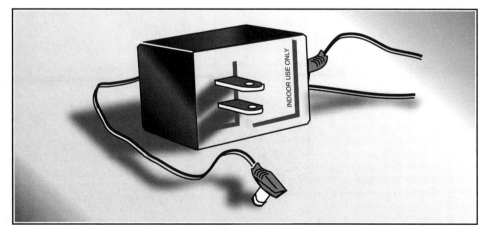

Figure 2.1 Power Transformer

21

Always use the transformer that comes with a piece of equipment, sometimes simply called the unit. If a unit's transformer is unavailable, check that the voltage and maximum current rating on the replacement transformer matches the recommended voltage and rating on the unit itself. The power level is labeled on both the transformer and the jack on the unit. Never use a transformer whose voltage doesn't correspond with that of the piece of equipment. Equipment that uses transformers might have a slight hum.

GROUNDING

Ground loops occur when different circuits are grounded to different ground potentials, which may create a hum. For proper grounding, plug all equipment into the same circuit box, or ground potential.

Sometimes simply flipping the ground switch on the direct box, or connecting the instrument or amplifier to a ground potential using an alligator clip will stop the hum. Single coil pickups on guitars may hum depending on where the musician is standing. The musician may have to turn and face a different direction to find the quietest spot. Fluorescent lights are notorious for creating a grounding hum. Some studios hum due to improper grounding. As a last resort, isolate the grounding post on the plug with a ground lifter (Figure 2.2).

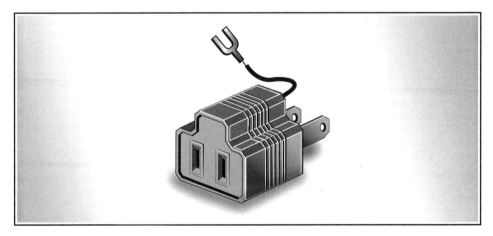

Figure 2.2 Ground Lifter

A ground lifter is an adapter that fits between the plug at the end of the AC cord, and the electrical wall input, and removes the grounding post. For optimum performance and minimal electric shock to the musician, properly ground every piece of equipment. But a ground lifter is not recommended, as it may give someone a serious electrical shock, Mind you, a guitarist might play one heck of a solo with 117 volts surging through his fingers.

BATTERIES

Many items such as direct boxes, guitar pedals and effects run on batteries, usually 9-volt. The studio should keep a supply of new batteries in the tech shop. The number of batteries supplied by the studio may need to be written down on the work order, and charged to the client. Sometimes, when equipment has the option of batteries, use them over a transformer, as the signal tends to be cleaner, with minimal interference or hum.

Whenever changing batteries, mark the date on the battery using a piece of adhesive tape. Then you, or whoever changes the battery, will know when it was last changed. If a 9-volt battery is not labeled, check its power level with a battery checker. Every studio should have a battery checker. Don't use the old trick of putting the battery on your tongue to check it. This is unreliable, and should really only be done when checking the battery in your car.

POWER UP

Before beginning any setup, turn on all the equipment. Start with the console, if necessary, then turn on the tape machines, the outboard equipment, and finally the power amplifiers that drive the cue systems, and the studio and control room monitors. (Some studios leave the console and amplifiers on all the time.) Power amplifiers are always the last to be turned on before the session, and first to be turned off at the end of the day. Before turning anything on, mute the console's master gain in the control room and all sends to the headphones. The power spike from the amplifiers being turned on may blow the elements in speakers and headphones. Never turn a power amplifier on or off while anyone is wearing headphones. This gives new meaning to the term "getting one's ears pierced."

INPUT/SETUP SHEETS

The information on this input/setup sheet, Figures 2.3 and 2.4 will be referred to throughout this manual to set up the studio and control room for the engineer. This is an example, and not the only way to do the job. Session procedures vary widely from studio to studio.

The engineer will leave an input/setup sheet indicating what instruments will be used, his choice of microphones and their inputs to the console. Also included will be how he wants the console set up, including busses and cue sends. See Chapter Six for more on busses and cue sends. Sometimes effects sends and returns and outboard equipment are indicated. Any equipment rentals, different machine alignments, and other specific details regarding setup may also be included.

If the engineer doesn't contact the studio with the session information, telephone him. If you can't reach him, set up the equipment as best you can. If needed, call a senior assistant for help. Avoid doing nothing. An wrong setup is better than no setup. If the engineer is a regular at your studio, he may leave a stock sheet with the specific setups he uses.

Before any large setup begins, make a few photocopies of the input/setup sheet. Leave copies in the studio and the control room. It's amazing how easily the only copy can get lost. Perhaps even hide a copy away in your files for future reference. If you are fortunate enough to have a runner helping with the setup, give him a copy to get started.

Once the control room is cleaned and ready, and all equipment is turned on and warming up, use the input/setup sheet to start setting up the studio. Again, as session setup and protocol vary widely, it is not possible to detail every event you will encounter. This is a basic overview; there are many different instrument combinations and situations. Whatever works best for the musicians is almost always the right way. Depending on the needs of the project, the engineer might—

- Record and keep all instruments during basics.

- Record one instrument at a time until the songs are complete.

- Record a full rhythm section, only to replace and/or repair all the other instruments except the drums during overdubs. Sometimes other players play along only to help the drummer with the song structure, and to help him stay "in the groove." These other tracks, or sections of them, might be kept and used as they may have a feel that gets lost during overdubs.

  Any overdubs or repairs on these other tracks are usually recorded once the choice drum take is established. This choice take can be either one complete take or sections of different takes edited together. (A take in the studio usually refers to a recorded performance. A pass usually refers to the process of recording. For example, making a copy from one machine to another is called pass, not a take.)

  Sounds are written down using a setup sheet so the session can return to the same sounds, if necessary, and repair these tracks. (See Chapter Nine for more on setup sheets.) Of course, you aren't really "writing down the sound." This term refers to writing down the equipment names and settings used in getting a particular sound.

- Program a computer to play all the parts at once.

- Simply set up all the instruments in the studio and play with no isolation or headphones, with amplifiers blaring, the way Elvis used to do it.

For overdubs, an input/setup sheet is not always necessary as the setup tends to be less involved than basics. It is not uncommon for the assistant to do a general setup, then wait for the engineer to arrive before fine tuning the setup. As the engineer does a monitor mix in the control room, the assistant sets up for the overdub in the studio. As well, setup and breakdown of equipment happens throughout the session, not just before the session, as with basics.

AEH	ARTIST _Tuff Beans_		DATE _July 31, Year_		
	PRODUCER _Bob Loblaw_		STUDIO A [X] B [ ] C [ ]		
	ENGINEER _Casey Jones_		ASSISTANT _A. Reader_		

INSTRUMENT	MICROPHONE	PARAMETER	INPUT	BUSS	OUTBOARD
Bass Guitar Amp	U - 47	Cardioid	1	2	
Bass Guitar Direct	DI Box		2	3	
Kick Drum	421		3	4	EQ 1 → Lim 1
Snare Drum - Top	SM 57		5	5	EQ 2
Snare Drum - Bottom	451		6	5	EQ 3
High Hat	451	-10 dB PAD	7	6	
Tom-Toms - Low	421		8	7	
Mid	421		9	7,8	
High	421		10	8	
Overhead Ride	U - 87	Cardioid	11	9	
Overhead Crash 1	U - 87	Cardioid	12	10	
Overhead Crash 2	U - 87	Cardioid	13	9,10	
Ambiance 1 - L	414	Cardioid	14	11	
Ambiance 1 - R	414	Cardioid	15	12	
Ambiance 2 - L	U - 87	Cardioid	16	11	
Ambiance 2 - R	U - 87	Cardioid	17	12	
Guitar 1 - Amp	421		18	15	
Guitar 1 - Direct	DI Box		19	15	
Guitar 2	SM - 57	-10 dB PAD	20	16	
Keyboard 1 - L	Direct	MIDI to	21	19	
Keyboard 1 - R	Direct		22	20	
Keyboard 2 - L	Direct		23	19	
Keyboard 2 - R	Direct		24	20	
Reference Vocal	U - 87		25		
Talkback			31	1	
Click			Direct to 23		
STEREO CUE 1	Guitars, Keys, and Bass				
STEREO CUE 2	Drums				
SEND 3	ECHO CHAMBER 1 L		Line in 27		
	ECHO CHAMBER 1 R		Line in 28		

Figure 2.3 Input/Setup Sheet

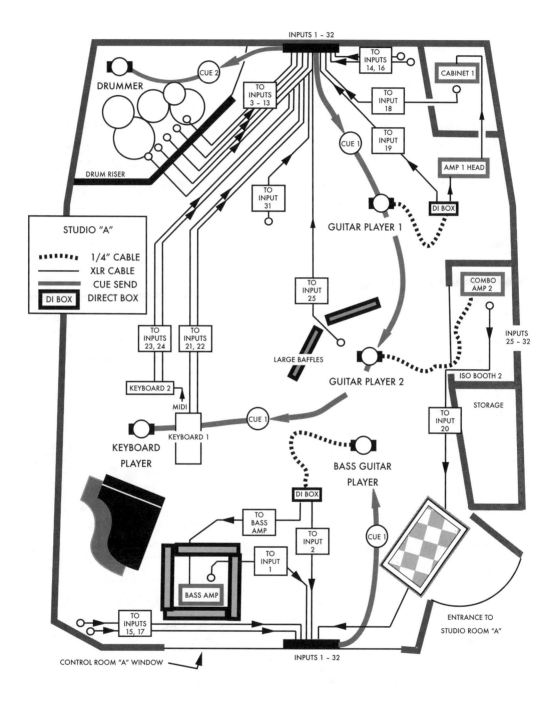

INPUTS 1 – 32

CUE 2

DRUMMER

TO INPUTS 3 – 13

TO INPUTS 14, 16

CABINET 1

TO INPUT 18

TO INPUT 19

CUE 1

AMP 1 HEAD

DRUM RISER

TO INPUT 31

GUITAR PLAYER 1

DI BOX

STUDIO "A"

🞄🞄🞄🞄🞄🞄🞄 1/4" CABLE
———— XLR CABLE
———— CUE SEND
DI BOX DIRECT BOX

TO INPUT 25

COMBO AMP 2

INPUTS 25 – 32

TO INPUTS 23, 24

TO INPUTS 21, 22

LARGE BAFFLES

GUITAR PLAYER 2

ISO BOOTH 2

KEYBOARD 2

STORAGE

MIDI

CUE 1

TO INPUT 20

KEYBOARD PLAYER

KEYBOARD 1

BASS GUITAR

PLAYER

DI BOX

TO BASS AMP

CUE 1

TO INPUT 2

TO INPUT 1

BASS AMP

ENTRANCE TO STUDIO ROOM "A"

TO INPUTS 15, 17

CONTROL ROOM "A" WINDOW

INPUTS 1 – 32

Figure 2.4 *Back of Input/Setup Sheet*

PLACING MUSICAL INSTRUMENTS

Some of the items in the studio that you don't regularly handle are the musical instruments. You set up the microphones, stands, cables, amplifiers and heads for the amplifiers. You may plug in the effects the musician will be using. You may even be required to go out to the amplifier and turn it up a notch, but the musicians will usually arrive with their instruments and set them up. You are only expected to haul the instruments in their cases to their correct location in the studio.

Don't handle or remove an instrument from its case without the owner's permission, and even then, care is of the utmost importance. Never play someone's instrument without first asking. If you do need to handle any of the musical instruments, keep in mind that a musician uses his instrument to make a living, like a carpenter uses a hammer, a doctor uses a scalpel, or a record producer uses a telephone. The tremendous amounts of time spent playing a beloved instrument can sometimes create an unnatural bond between the musician and the instrument.

ROAD CASES

Most larger musical instruments and equipment travel in road cases. These are strong moveable boxes with wheels used to store, protect, and transport equipment. Road cases contain amplifiers, musical instruments, computers, and accessories such as cables, tuners, strings, picks, keys, etc. When these cases arrive for the session, take them into the studio. If the studio is in use, place the road cases in a corner out of the way until the studio is available.

Often road cases are stuffed full of equipment. Once the contents have been removed, this Pandora's box may be next to impossible to repack correctly without some sort of chart or list of contents. When unloading a road case filled with various kinds of equipment, make a list of everything removed, the order in which they came out, and maybe even a drawing of how everything was packed. The day will come toward the end of the project when everything that was in the road cases must be accounted for and repacked.

Store the empty road cases in an out-of-the-way place, such as a corner of the studio, or a separate storage area. If the cases stay in the studio, cover them with a packing blanket to prevent any buckles from rattling.

DRUMS

The heaviest and bulkiest of the instruments, such as drums, amplifiers, and piano are placed first. Drums, like most instruments, are commonly left to the player or his drum technician to assemble. Show the drummer the correct placement, according to the setup sheet, and help haul the road cases into the studio. Setting the drums up correctly can be challenging for the assistant, as every drummer sets up his kit differently. Studios that own and use a certain set of drums, learn how to set the drums up properly. One day a drummer will arrive for the session with just his drumsticks, expecting to sit down and play.

Before starting the setup, find out if the engineer wants a carpet or large mat under the drum kit. It's far easier to lay out a carpet before the drums are in place. A sandbag, or something similarly heavy and stable may be placed in or in front of the kick drum to keep the kit from slowly sliding forward during the session.

Some drummers hit the drums hard enough to warrant duct taping the cymbal stands and snare drum stand to the floor, or carpet to ensure they remain stationary throughout the session. Before doing anything this drastic, check with the engineer or musician after the kit is in place. If the pedals for the kick drum or high-hat squeak, bring in some oil and place it near the kit. Let the drummer or his drum tech oil the pedals.

Different songs may require different drum sounds, so a drummer might have more than one of each drum with him. Keep these extra drums out of the way and covered. Drums with snares may buzz and rattle, and this sound can leak into the microphones.

When snare drums are not in use, for instance, overnight, remove the tension on the snares under the drum, but again, check with the drummer first. Once all the drums are in place, move on to the guitar amplifier setup.

AMPLIFIERS

Guitar amplifiers come in two different styles: combination, or simply combo amplifiers, and split amplifiers. Combo amplifiers house the amplification section and the speaker cabinet section in one unit. Split amplifiers are broken down into two separate sections:

1) The power section, also called the head (or top), where the controls such as volume and tone are located.

2) The cabinet section, also called the bottom, where the speakers are.

These two sections are connected via heavy gauge speaker cable. The head can be stacked on top of the bottom cabinet for convenience, or the cabinet can be placed elsewhere. Placing the speaker cabinet away from the rest of the studio isolates the cabinet, while the head stays with the musician. Separating the cabinet from the head also prevents the head from being damaged by cabinet vibrations.

During overdubs, the musician might be in the control room with the head, while the cabinet is out in the studio or in an isolation booth. Some musicians will stay next to the cabinet, as this is how they rehearse and perform. Some players stand by their amplifiers to use the feedback as part of their guitar sound. No matter where the musician is, he will probably need to reach the controls such as tone, volume, standby, and maybe when checking his tuning.

Of course, different situations in the studio may require more than one cabinet or head, and in many different configurations. Sometimes one head feeds two speaker cabinets and each is recorded on separate tracks. The combinations are endless.

After finding out who will use which amplifier, wheel the road cases to the general areas where they will be placed, remove the amplifier from the road case, and place it correctly. According to our example input/setup sheet, there are three amplifiers being used for this basic session.

BASS AMPLIFIER

Baffle the bass guitar amplifier off to prevent the sound from leaking into other microphones in the rest of the studio, and to prevent the sound from the rest of the amplifiers from being picked up in the bass guitar amplifier microphone. See later in this chapter for more on baffles. The baffles are set up after the amplifiers are in place. If more isolation booths are available, the amplifier might be placed in one. It is common to isolate amplifiers for recording. As the bass amplifier is being placed, leave enough space behind and beside it for the baffles. Then move on to the next setup.

GUITAR 1 AMPLIFIER

According to the input/setup sheet, the amplifier to be used for guitar player 1 is a split amplifier. The cabinet section is put in isolation booth 1, while the head stays with the musician in the studio. Place a small table near the musician to hold the head, along with any accessories for the guitar player.

GUITAR 2 AMPLIFIER

The amplifier used for guitar player 2 is not split, according to the input/setup sheet illustration, so assume it's a combo amplifier. This amplifier is placed in isolation booth 2. At this point, just place the amplifiers, don't connect them and don't turn on the power.

After all the amplifiers are placed, plug them into the nearest electrical power box. Always use the power cable that comes with the amplifier. Don't turn the amplifier on without the instrument connected to it. Better yet, let the musician turn on his amplifier. Place a table nearby for this guitar player as well.

PIANO

Try to place the piano first, since it can be difficult to maneuver it through a studio full of cables, microphone stands, and baffles. Most larger studios have at least one piano. The input/setup sheet states that the piano is not being used for this basic session, so move it into a corner out of the way. Cover it with blankets as the strings may ring out sympathetically during the session.

If the piano is being used, it would be placed for the session, and a piano tuner might come in before the session to tune it. It wouldn't be moved again, since moving a piano may throw it out of tune. Sometimes, after a piano is set up and the microphones are correctly placed, the piano is baffled off and covered with blankets for isolation. The piano player then stays in the studio with the rest of the musicians, with no worry of leakage to or from other microphones.

Occasionally clean the piano with a soft chamois and some furniture polish. Never dip it in soapy water and hose it down.

ORGANS

Some organs are quite bulky and require amplification, either from an internal speaker, or from an external *Leslie*. A Leslie is a speaker system much like a traditional guitar amplifier, only with rotating horn speakers inside. The speed of rotation is determined by the musician playing the instrument. A Leslie can be used to amplify any instrument, including a guitar. The cabinet is sometimes isolated, and recorded much like a guitar amplifier.

ELECTRONIC KEYBOARDS

According to the input/setup sheet, the keyboards are MIDI'd to each other. (See Chapter Three for more on MIDI.) Most pro players will have enough stands to hold all their keyboards, but an extra stand, or even a small table may be needed for additional keyboards.

Again, the musician usually sets up his own instrument. Show the player where his station will be. Sometimes the electronic keyboards are played in the control room, as normally they require no amplification, just direct signal into the console.

ADDITIONAL INSTRUMENTS

After all the larger instruments, amplifiers, and baffles are in place, bring in the remaining instruments, such as individual guitars, horns, etc. Place these instruments within easy reach of the musicians. Leave these instruments in their road cases, and let the musicians deal with them.

A musician may have more than one instrument out and ready to be played. If an acoustic stringed instrument is set up and not being played during the recording, tell the engineer; he may want the musician to put it away, or cover it with a towel to prevent it from ringing out sympathetically. Acoustic instruments in the control room should be covered, as loud monitors will cause the strings to ring out.

TUNERS

Tuners are essential for most stringed instruments in the studio unless the musician has perfect pitch and does all the tuning by ear, or the music is more important than the tuning—such as when Bob Dylan records.

When I was assistant engineer on Bob Dylan's "Empire Burlesque" he asked me to help tune his guitar before an overdub. (Yet another of the assistant's never-ending duties.) When I had tuned the E, B, and G strings, Bob took the guitar away saying he was going to play only those strings. Most players make sure all strings are in tune to take advantage of sympathetic ringing of other strings—not Bob.

Musicians stay in tune throughout a session by using a consistently reliable tuner. There are presently three kinds of tuners—

- A tuning fork. This is a U-shaped device with a metal handle that when struck, produces a fixed tone in perfect pitch, commonly A-440.

- An electronic tuner. These are quite popular today not only because they are reasonably priced, but because they are easy to use and reliable. Electronic tuners commonly have automatic calibration, an internal tuning tone, a built-in microphone and a line input. Most digital guitar amplifier simulators have a built in tuner.

- A strobe tuner. These use a revolving disc with various slots located at exact distances from each other. When the disc turns at certain speeds, the slots become a single line. Think of watching the spokes of a wagon wheel. As the wheel turns, the spokes or lines appear to be slowly revolving forward or backward. When the lines on the strobe appear stationary, the note is in tune.

A strobe tuner needs to be calibrated every time it is moved or turned on. Historically, a tuning fork has been used to calibrate a strobe tuner. If no tuning fork is available, send a continuous single tone to the tuner from either a variable oscillator, or a pure A-440 tone from a keyboard output.

Once the tuner is calibrated, record a section of the calibration tone on one track of the multitrack, usually where the alignment tones are. The tape label, Figure 8.4, shows a 30 second tuning tone. This tone is used for the complete project as a reliable source of reference to calibrate all tuners. (See Chapter Eight for more on tuning tones.)

Access the input of the tuner with either a line input or a microphone. Most strobe tuners come with a microphone, kept in a small slot in the back of the tuner. Most tuners have an input and an output, so the signal can go through the tuner before being recorded, allowing the tuner to stay active. However, many engineers do not want the extra processing of a tuner in the signal path being recorded. The engineer may choose to assign a buss on the instrument input channel from the console directly to the input of the tuner.

STUDIO EQUIPMENT SETUP

BAFFLES

For some recordings, such as basics, certain instruments might be isolated from the rest of the instruments to avoid unwanted leakage into other microphones and unwanted leakage from other instruments. Figure 2.5 shows that baffles are heavy movable walls used to isolate a musician or instrument and prevent unwanted leakage to or from other microphones from within the studio.

Baffles are used not only to isolate a sound, but also to deaden certain areas of the studio. One side of the baffle is usually hard wood, for a more reflective sound, and the other side is cloth, for more absorbency. The engineer will decide which way he wants the baffles to face.

Larger baffles may have windows in the top half, so an isolated singer can see the rest of the session during basics. For vocal overdubs, baffles might be placed behind a singer to prevent the ambiance of the studio from being picked up in the vocal microphone.

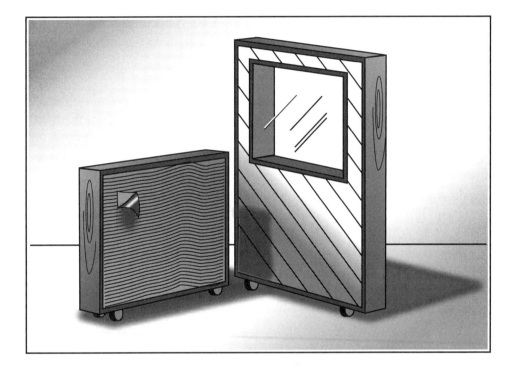

Figure 2.5 Baffles

Place the large baffles very early in the setup. Don't roll the baffles over cables, or between all the delicate musical instruments. Baffles can be large enough to be awkward and unstable. Imagine the consequences of a 200—pound baffle falling onto a carefully placed Stradivarius. A million-dollar antique would become a pile of very expensive toothpicks.

Smaller baffles can be used to build an isolation booth for amplifiers, such as the setup for the bass guitar on the input/setup sheet. To isolate an amplifier, place the baffles around three sides of it. If the baffles have wheels, turn them over on their sides. The isolation is much better, and they won't roll away during the bass solo.

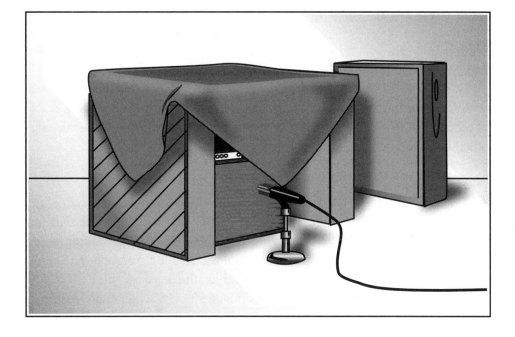

Figure 2.6 Baffles Creating an Isolation Booth

Figure 2.6 shows another baffle on top of the three walls, making a roof. Leave the front baffle open for the musician and engineer to access the controls and microphone. After the microphone is in place, close the open side with another baffle and cover the booth with packing blankets to ensure isolation.

Some studios have small movable isolation booths. These usually have no windows, can be placed anywhere in the studio, and can house an amplifier and its microphones. Once the setup inside the booth is complete, the door is closed to isolate the contents totally from the rest of the studio.

According to the input/setup sheet, the large baffles being used for the singer won't totally isolate him. Although a small amount of leakage may be recorded, the singer—guitar player 2 as noted on the input/setup sheet—has freedom to walk around. The musicians' freedom to move about usually takes precedence over isolation.

Of course the band can be heard in the background on the vocal track recorded during basics. This vocal is referred to as the guide vocal, also called the live vocal, and is commonly not used in the final mix.

CHAIRS

When setting up for a larger session, chairs may be needed for all the players. Placing chairs after the baffles have been set up allows you to see where all the musicians will be located, and where the microphone stands will be placed. As a rule of thumb, the larger the session, the earlier you set up the chairs. On most smaller sessions, a stack of chairs can be left in a corner, so if a musician needs one, he simply asks you, or grabs one for himself. However, for any session, large or small, if any musical instrument requires the musician to be seated, for example a cello player, place the chair before the musician arrives. Once the chairs are in place, begin setting up the microphone stands.

MICROPHONE STANDS

Microphone stands are used to position microphones exactly where the engineer wants, and to ensure the microphones stay there for the duration of the recording. When setting up microphone stands—

- Use stable, reliable, well balanced stands that will work with the instrument. All connections on the stands must be tight, but not too tight. If the connections on a stand won't grip, don't use adhesive tape to hold the microphone at the correct height. Just replace the stand. No matter how much tape is used, the weight of the microphone will eventually cause the grip to loosen. No one wants to watch a microphone slowly sink onto the strings of the piano during a fantastic take.

- Place the microphone stands throughout the studio according to the input/setup sheet, keeping in mind the instruments to be recorded. For violins, you would place the microphones above the musicians. For French horns, you would place them behind the musicians.

- Use smaller stands with good maneuverability for exact microphone placement in front of the amplifiers.

- Set all stands squarely on the floor, not resting on other stands. They must be solidly placed so they will not move.

- Don't try to connect a microphone to a stand that is in a difficult-to-reach position. Bring the microphone end of the boomstand to you, or risk dropping a sensitive microphone while leaning over to change it. If the microphone has already been exactly placed and you are changing it, try not to move the location of the stand. Find a good spot to make the change without being in a precarious position.

- Ask the engineer his preference. While recording vocals or acoustic instruments, some engineers may want the microphone suspended from a boom, rather than resting on a stand. They may feel that the diaphragm within the microphone should hang, not rest on anything, as it does when the microphone sits upright.

- Use matching stands and mounts when setting up stereo microphones, such as matched overhead microphones. Don't use one boom stand and one regular stand.

- Position the counterweight on a boomstand high enough to avoid someone accidentally hitting their head.

- Don't place the drum stands before the drums are set up.

- When you are placing a microphone on a table, such as during an interview, use the smallest stand possible. Some microphones, such as lavalier, don't need a stand, as they are clipped directly on the lapel.

. . . .

Summary

Chapter Two explained what is involved in preparing the studio for a basic session:

- Stocking the control room and studio with all necessary stationary items used throughout the session.

- Understanding the input/setup sheet to set up the studio.

- Bringing in and placing all musical instruments and amplifiers.

- Correctly placing baffles, chairs and microphone stands.

3

CHAPTER THREE

. . . .

Cables, Microphones and Levels

When standing inside a nice clean modern recording studio, there is no indication that trenches beneath the floor and behind the surrounding walls are teeming with audio cables. These cables carry all signals throughout the studio and control room to the console and patchbay. Most cables are permanently hard wired and changed or accessed only by qualified technical personnel. As these cables are not routinely accessed for setup of a session, this is not the time to discuss them.

LEVELS

Before we start lugging and plugging cables, let's go over a few basics about signal processing, the decibel and various levels.

SIGNAL PROCESSING

All studio equipment is designed to work within certain limits. Figure 3.1 shows that all audio signal processors have—

- Distortion point. Also called clipping, overload, or reaching the saturation point, distortion occurs when analog tape or an electronic device such as a pre-amplifier, console, outboard gear, amplifier or speaker is driven beyond its designed limits. This is a basic explanation as there are many different forms of distortion. You want harmonics to come from the music, not the audio device.

- Headroom. The distance, measured in decibels, between a device's optimum operating level and the distortion point. More headroom can mean more room for peaks.

- Optimum operating level. An audio device's optimum operating level, usually indicated by 0VU on the device's meter. This is where the signal is cleanest with the least amount of distortion. VU, or volume units and the decibel may appear to be numerically equivalent, but they are certainly different.

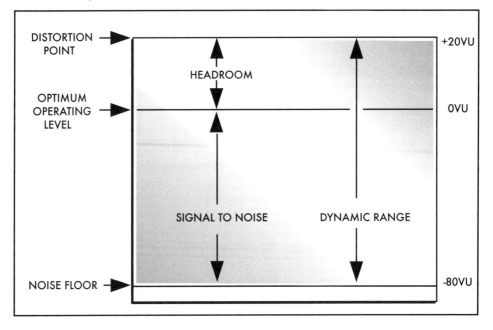

Figure 3.1 Breakdown of an Audio Device

- Noise floor. The amount of noise a device produces with no signal going through it. Every electrical device—think of your refrigerator—generates its own internal noise. Manufacturers try to make this sound as low as possible, but it still exists.

- Signal to noise ratio. The ratio, measured in decibels, between the optimum signal level and the noise floor. A higher number is desired here so more information can be recorded. Figure 3.1 shows the signal to noise ratio is 80dB.

- Dynamic range. The distance between the noise floor and the distortion point of an audio circuit, also measured in decibels. If the circuit begins to distort once the input level reaches +20dB, then the dynamic range is 100dB.

THE DECIBEL

The decibel, dB, in simple form, uses a linear scale to measure non-linear levels. It is a ratio, a comparison of one number to another, in reference to a predetermined 0dB level. In reference to human hearing, 0dBSPL (Sound Pressure Level) is, in theory, silence—the threshold of hearing. In reality, the actual threshold of adult hearing is roughly 20dBSPL. When using the decibel to reference voltage, 0dBv is not all the way off, but a predetermined level of .775 volts. All levels are referred to as plus or minus from this 0 reference point.

The decibel is used to assess, among other levels, sound pressure (dBSPL), voltage (dBv), power (dBu), digital levels (dBFS) and more. Let's look at dBSPL. We all know how frequencies on a piano rise exponentially, in that they double every octave (220Hz, 440Hz, 880Hz, 1760Hz...) At a certain point, sound pressure levels begin to rise similarly, and can get very high. The decibel makes these very high or very low ratios more manageable.

Using the logarithmic scale divided by ten (*deci*), Alexander Graham Bell (*bel*), translated the exponential, or non-linear SPL scale to the linear dBSPL scale. Using *micro*pascals (*u*Pa) he determined that as the SPL rose exponentially (100*u*Pa, 1,000*u*Pa, 10,000*u*Pa, 100,000*u*Pa...) the equivalent decibel scale rose linearly (20dB, 40dB, 60dB, 80dB...) This basic primer should be a starting point for your clear understanding of the decibel.

Figure 3.2 shows the SPL, the equivalent decibel level and the sound references. Note that the doubling of SPL equals an increase of 6dB, no matter what that pressure level is. For example, one instrument might create a level of 40,000*u*Pa, or 72dBSPL. Bring in another one, and it doubles the SPL to 80,000 *u*Pa, raising the level by 6dB to 78dBSPL.

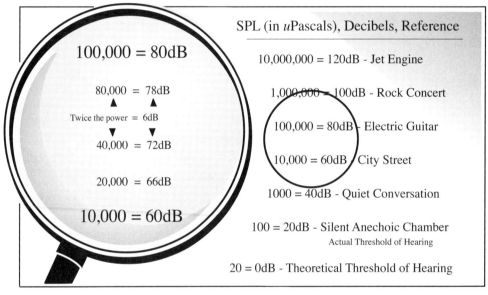

Figure 3.2 SPL vs Decibel

LEVELS

Different needs and uses dictate that an incoming signal level can be interpreted in many ways. Figure 3.3 shows a microphone placed in front of a singer. He sings a note that sustains at about 72dBSPL. (The reference represents levels only—independent of frequency.) That signal can be interpreted as—

• SPL. About 40,000*u*Pa.

• dBSPL. According to Figure 3.2, 40,000*u*Pa would be about 72dBSPL, or simply 72dB.

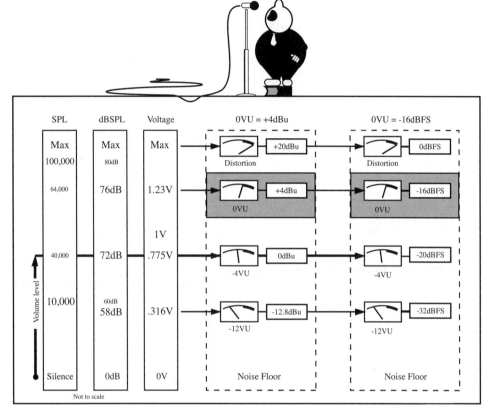

Figure 3.3 *Signal Levels*

- Voltage. When sound vibrates the membrane inside the microphone, those pressure levels translate into voltage. In this case, the equivalent input voltage is .775v which is predetermined to be 0dBu.

- 0VU = +4dBu. 0VU on professional level consoles is +4dB over the 0 dBu reference point. 1.23V = 76dB = 0VU
  When the singer reaches 76dB, the input meter reads 0VU.

- 0VU = -16dBFS. The digital input level uses yet another reference. 0dBFS (Full Scale) is the loudest possible level that can be stored digitally before distortion. Digital recording equipment uses a 0VU reference standard from -12dB to -18dB below this point, depending on the situation.

DIGITAL/ANALOG DISTORTION

There is a distinct difference between analog and digital distortion. With analog recording, as the signal saturates the tape, the gradual increase of distortion can add a certain warm compressed sound. When recording in the digital medium, louder levels, just below 0dBFS, results in the most transparent and smoothest sounding conversion from analog to digital. Once that threshold is reached, the resulting distortion is unpleasant and unusable.

THE SOUND ENVELOPE

The envelope is the time it takes a sound to reach its maximum power point, then die down. This growth and decay pattern contains the harmonic content, or shape of the sound. The sound envelope is function of level, not frequency, so it can be modified using compression and limiting. Every envelope is different, except of course, for a sample. Figure 3.4 shows how a guitar strum is broken down into: attack or growth time—the time it takes a sound to reach its initial peak, or maximum level; decay—the time it takes the initial peaks to die down; sustain—the length the note is held; release—the time it takes for the signal to die down.

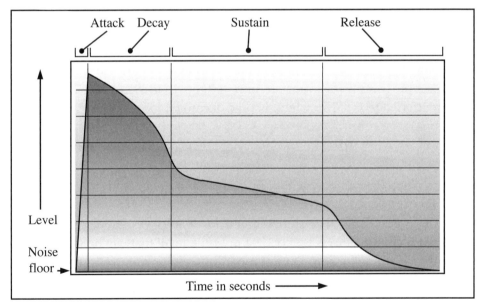

Figure 3.4 Sound Envelope

CABLES

Although there are many different cable formats used in the recording studio, the main ones the assistant deals with daily are XLR (also called cannon), RCA, ¼", MIDI, and digital specific cables, such as USB, S/PDIF, co-axial, and lightpipe. There are others, but these are the most commonly used.

BALANCED CABLES

A standard recording studio 'balanced' cable uses three wires—two to carry the signal and one for the ground. Note that the cable itself is not balanced, the system is balanced. The three wires are termed hot, cold and common. XLR cables and ¼" stereo cables are balanced. On a balanced ¼" cable, the three wires connected are TRS, tip, ring and sleeve with the sleeve being the ground (Figure 3.5).

XLR cables are low impedance balanced lines used to carry a line or microphone level audio signal from microphone to console, console to multitrack, plus many other combinations.

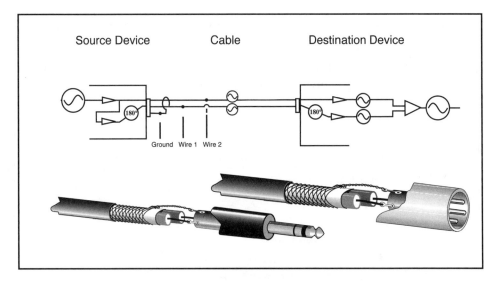

Figure 3.5 *Balanced Cable*

XLR cables house a male connector at one end and a female connector at the other. Signal flows in the direction of the pins, with the male sending the signal, and the female receiving it. A lot like dating.

Two of the three wires are for signal flow and the third is for ground, or shield. Of the two wires that carry signal, one has the polarity (phase) switched. Why? As any rogue interference will affect both wires simultaneously, when signal phase is reversed at the other end, errant signals picked up along the way will be switched out of phase, and canceled out. This process, called "balancing" or common mode rejection, eliminates interference, enabling the use of longer cables with minimal signal degradation.

Figure 3.5 shows a source device, then a balanced cable, and then a destination device. See how the single incoming signal source is split into two, then switched out of phase. Signal flows through the cable and, at the destination device, the signal is combined where the phase is switched back, and continues on to its way.

UNBALANCED CABLES

Figure 3.6 shows 'unbalanced' RCA and ¼" cables. Both contain two wires—one is hot, and the other is the shield, which is wrapped around the hot wire and used as a ground. Again, the term 'unbalanced cable' is misleading. The cable is not unbalanced, the system is unbalanced.

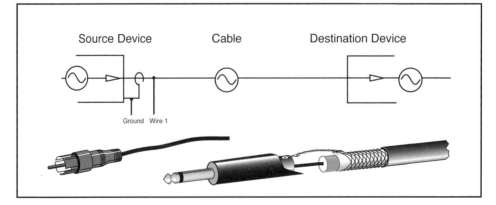

Figure 3.6 Unbalanced Cables

These high impedance cables are normally used for sending mono signal from the instrument to the amplifier or direct box. (See later in this chapter for more on impedance.)

Most outboard equipment uses ¼" inputs, and all consoles have the option of balanced and unbalanced ¼" line level inputs. The signal in an unbalanced line weakens with increased length, and has no protection against RF (radio frequency) interference. Better to use the shorter heavier gauge cables.

RCA cables are used on most home and semi-professional recording equipment such as tuners and CD players. These cables operate at a lower power level (-10dBu, unbalanced) than professional recording equipment (+4dBu, balanced.) If needed, this signal level must be increased to conform with the console's input level. An adapter box may be used to bring the signal from -10dBu up to +4dBu. Once the signal is at the correct operating level, it can be properly integrated into the console and the rest of the studio equipment through the patchbay.

Additional unbalanced lines include ¼" non-shielded cables, such as speaker cables. These cables are simply two heavy gauge parallel wires. Don't mix them up with shielded cables. These cables go from amplifier to speaker, and must be heavy gauge for as little resistance as possible.

MIDI CABLES

MIDI (Musical Instrument Digital Interface) cables are five-pin cables used to interface computers, keyboards, drum machines, samplers, and some outboard equipment. Data, including notes, length of notes, velocity, pitch change, modulation, attack, release, filters, and presets is sent through the MIDI cable from the master to the slaves. The slaves then duplicate the master, playing whatever it plays. Better keyboards, drum machines and DAWs are completely integrated with MIDI, and are very easy to connect using proper MIDI cables. A healthy understanding of any and all MIDI equipment in your studio is highly recommended.

IMPEDANCE

Resistance, or impedance, is a device's natural physical opposition to electrical power and, along with voltage and current, is measured in ohms (Ω). Almost all recording studio microphones are low impedance, commonly 150Ω—300Ω. In the studio, different impedance levels must be interconnected in various combinations for the cleanest sounds. Low impedance cables can be extended for longer lengths without significant signal loss.

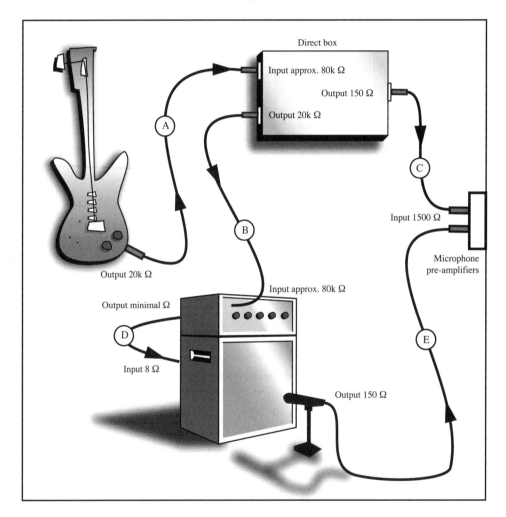

Figure 3.7 Impedance Differences

We know that cables connect a source and a destination of a signal. Traditionally, both the source and the destination impedance's were matched at 600Ω. But it was found that a source device with a low output impedance connected to a destination device with a much higher input impedance, at least ten times as high as the source device, was more efficient for studio applications. Figure 3.7 shows the cable impedance differences in a standard guitar setup. Your numbers will be slightly different than in this example:

- Cable A. An unbalanced ¼" guitar cable going from the output of the guitar into the input of the direct box. (See later in this chapter for more on the direct box.) The source impedance, the guitar is 20kΩ, and the destination impedance, the direct box is 80kΩ—four times the source impedance.

- Cable B. An unbalanced ¼" guitar cable going from the direct box output to the input of the guitar amplifier. This output simply routes the guitar signal through the direct box. The source impedance is 20kΩ, the destination impedance is approximately 80kΩ—about four times the source impedance.

- Cable C. A balanced XLR cable that connects the output of the direct box to the microphone input at the console. The source impedance is 150Ω, and the destination impedance is 1500Ω—ten times the source impedance.

- Cable D. A heavy gauge ¼" power cable going from the output of the amplifier head to the input of the speaker cabinet. Here, the source impedance is minimal, and the destination impedance is 8Ω—over twice the source impedance.

- Cable E. A microphone to the input of the console pre-amplifier. The source, the microphone is 150Ω, the input to the console is 1500Ω—again, ten times the source impedance. Impedance levels between microphone and pre-amplifier must be kept as low as possible to minimize any RF interference and maximize transfer of electrical signal.

GROUND

Electric signal flows using a source, a load, and a destination. The power supply is the source. The load uses this power and ultimately, the ground is the destination. This is the path of electrical flow. Most equipment today is fitted with three-prong outlets, the third being a chassis ground, to avoid any bothersome recording engineer electrocution issues.

Ground loop, or hum occurs when electrical equipment is grounded to more than one location, creating multiple paths. As well, hum originates from different sources such as fluorescent lights, video monitors, dimmer switches, refrigerators and more.

MICROPHONE INPUT PANELS

The studio is connected to the console via the microphone input panels. Microphone input panels, such as shown in Figure 3.8, are wall plates or movable boxes that connect the studio and control room to inputs and outputs of the console. Most input panels are broken into—

* XLR inputs. These allow microphones to connect directly to the console from anywhere within the studio, isolation booths, and control room. The numbers etched on the input panels correspond with the inputs at the console. For example, input 1 on the input panel is commonly 'normalled' to channel 1 on the console. (See Chapter Six for more on normals.)

* Cue send outputs. Signal also flows from the console to the headphone amplifiers to the stereo cue outputs on the input panel. These outputs are used for headphone mixes.

* MIDI ports. Some input panels house MIDI ports for quick connection to various MIDI equipment placed throughout the premises.

- Speaker ties. ¼" speaker ties are used mainly to connect amplifier heads to cabinets within the studio. This eliminates the need for long cables from going out through the control room door into the studio. Amplifier heads within the studio can also connect to cabinets elsewhere in the studio. For example, if the head is in one corner of the studio, and the cabinet is in an isolation booth across the room, they can be connected through the speaker ties on the input panels.

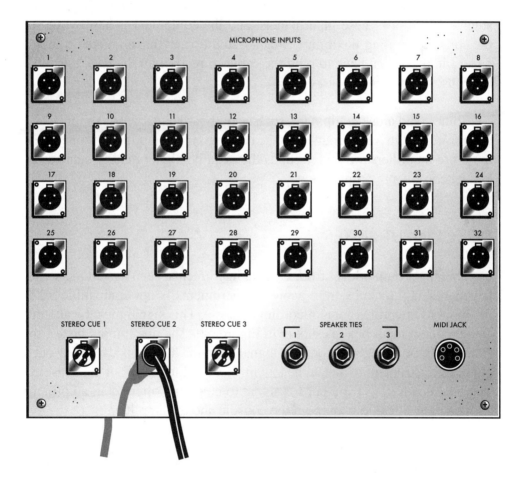

Figure 3.8 *Microphone Input Panel*

Larger studios have at least two input panels in the studio, and might have smaller input panels in the isolation booths and the control room. Chances are slim that many instruments would be set up in an isolation booth and the control room, so there is usually no need for a full input panel.

Additional input panels in the control room may allow access to the multitracks, or in some cases directly into A to D (analog to digital) convertors, the outboard equipment, and access to the console and patchbay. Some studios don't have these input panels, and the equipment is hard wired to the console, limiting flexibility. Smaller studios may have no studio input panels at all, so you have to plug the cables directly into the back panel of the console.

Some stand alone equipment, such as outboard equalizers, compressors and limiters have XLR inputs because they have pre-amplifiers. Sometimes these pre-amplifiers are preferred, as they can be higher quality than some budget console pre-amplifiers.

DIRECT INPUT BOXES

The direct output level from electric instruments, such as guitars, some keyboards, and pickups from acoustic instruments is not compatible with the input to the professional recording console. This signal must be altered using a direct input box, as shown in Figure 3.9. The direct input box, also called a DI, or direct box, converts signal from the high impedance 1/4" output of the instrument to match the low impedance input XLR of the console. The box also has a 1/4" output for signal to continue, often to an amplifier, allowing the signal to go to both the console and the amplifier.

Direct boxes are either active or passive. Active boxes contain batteries, and convert impedance one way, from high to low. Passive boxes, by nature of the transformer in them, can convert impedance both ways, high to low, and low to high.

Direct boxes may be used, among other applications, to send a low imped-ance signal from the console to a high impedance input of a guitar amplifier. This is sometimes done to add the sound of an amplifier to previously recorded tracks. Active direct boxes need power, either AC or batteries. If batteries are used, unplug cables into direct boxes during long periods of inactivity, such as overnight, to eliminate power drain on the batteries.

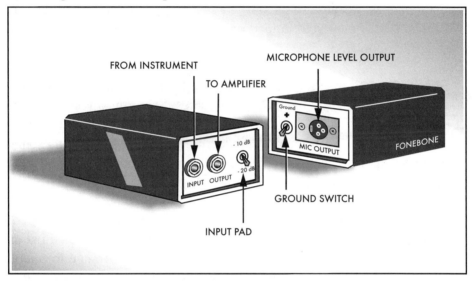

Figure 3.9 *Direct Box*

Direct boxes have a ground reverse switch used to stop electrical hums and buzzes. Most also have a pad switch, and some have a trim pot to set an exact operating level.

EFFECTS BOXES

The musician may want to insert additional signal processing devices into the signal before it is sent to the console, such as distortion pedals, additional equalization, fuzz, wah-wah etc. To do this, short ¼" cables are needed to connect them. He will also need additional power strips, or more batteries. It is standard for the players to supply their own cables.

RUNNING CABLES

BRINGING CABLES

With all the baffles, chairs and microphone stands set up, the next step is running the cables. On larger sessions, lay out the cables before placing the microphones. Because of the traffic and activity involved when running the cables, stands may get bumped or knocked over, perhaps damaging a delicate microphone.

Standard practice is to bring out and run all the XLR cables, then all the ¼" cables, then finally all the AC power cables. Sometimes you set up the XLR cables, the ¼" cables, and the power cables for each instrument, then move on to the next instrument. This lets a musician fine tune his sound while you set up the rest of the studio. A few points to ponder before a large session:

• Confirm that there are enough cables. This includes extension cords for electrical outlets, XLR cables, ¼" shielded cables and, if the situation calls for it, MIDI cables. If you are short on cables, arrange for more, either from elsewhere on the premises, or from a neighboring studio. The session should never have to stop due to lack of functional cables.

• Although there may be enough cables, some may be questionable. The rarely used cables in the studio are usually the thin flimsy ones, the short ones, and the ones with exposed wires. Always use the thickest, most reliable cables available.

• When you must use the thin questionable cables, use them on non-input items, such as headphones. If something goes wrong with the cable, the musician will instantly notice, and it won't affect the actual recording. If a questionable cable is used on a microphone, its breakdown may not be noticed immediately.

- Store cables according to length, maybe using colored tags for different lengths of cable.

- Use cables that are slightly longer than needed, as cables that are too short are easily tripped on. Never use a cable that is so short that it's taut. A musician tripping, falling, and breaking his neck is one thing, but think of the damage to the microphone and input panel. Better to extend it or exchange it for a longer cable than risk this kind of damage.

- Take into account the possibility of a guitarist moving into the control room for a track repair. Run the cables so he can simply walk into the control room from the studio, instrument in hand, and continue recording without any change in sound.

- Keep the studio's cables and the musician's cables separate. When a musician has his own ¼" cables, use them, but be sure to label them to avoid any mix ups. The musician should leave with everything he arrived with, except perhaps, his sanity.

- Bring out all the cables, and even a few extra so you won't have to go hunting around when you need them. Untie any knots in them, and place all the microphone cables on the floor near the input panels.

CONNECTIONS AND PLACEMENT

Now that all cables are in the studio, run them as described on the input/setup sheet, Figure 2.3. Notice how all the instruments are laid out, with the drums in one section, the guitars in another, the keyboards in another. This is to organize individual instruments at the console. Sometimes the engineer might skip an input, such as on a drum setup, in case an additional drum microphone needs to be introduced. This prevents a lone drum input coming in at the other end of the console.

Again, as all recording sessions differ, there are many ways to set up the equipment. The following setup is included only as a reference:

1) According to the input/setup sheet, the bass guitar setup has two inputs. One is a microphone in front of the amplifier, and the other is a direct signal from the bass guitar into the console. Remove the cable tie from the first XLR cable. A cable tie is a small piece of plastic or Velcro used to keep a cable properly wrapped when stored. It may be permanently fastened to one end of the XLR cable so it's always there when needed.

2) Grasp the cable's male end, and connect it to input 1 on the input panel. If the studio has more than one input panel, use the panel closest to the instrument.

3) The connectors, or jacks, have locks that keep them attached while plugged in. This lock will click when the cable is properly connected. After the click, gently tug on the cable to see if it is locked. If you don't hear a click when plugging in a cable, remove it from the input and try again.

4) With the remainder of the cable in your hand, walk over to the correct microphone stand, unraveling the cable as you go. When wrapped correctly, the cable should unravel with nary a knot or tangle. (See Chapter Twelve for more on wrapping cables.)

5) Leave the rest of the cable at the base of the microphone stand. If the stand needs to be moved, extra cable is at the base of the stand, not back at the wall. Hang the female end of the cable over its respective microphone stand. This leaves no doubt which cable connects to which microphone. Move on to the next cable.

6) According to the input/setup sheet, input 2 is not a microphone, but the output of a direct box. Place the direct box on the floor close to where the musician will be located. Run the next XLR cable from input 2 to the XLR output of the direct box, again leaving the excess cable on the floor near the direct box.

7) Connect one end of a ¼" cable to the input of the direct box and leave the other end loose for the musician to connect his instrument. A musician may prefer to use his own ¼" cable. On powered direct boxes, leave the cable unplugged, as it may drain the power.

8) Run a second ¼" cable from the high impedance output of the direct box to the input of the amplifier. Again, keep the length of ¼" cables to a minimum.

9) Connect the power cable from the amplifier to an AC outlet. Keep audio cables and electrical cables from running parallel, as this may introduce AC hum (60/50 Hz) into your low level audio signal. If theses cables must cross, lay them at right angles.

10) Leave the amplifier switched off. If the amplifier is turned on without the instrument connected, the power may load down and blow a fuse.

11) The bass guitar setup is now complete, except for the microphone, which you will bring in after running all the cables. When the musician arrives, he can plug in the instrument, turn on the amplifier and begin warming up.

12) The next instrument on the input/setup sheet is the drums. Plug the drum microphones into inputs 3 to 17, leaving input 4 open. Ensure that no two cables are accidentally plugged into the same input at different input panels.

13) Don't wrap the cables all neatly in a row across the floor as they can easily tangle, making them difficult to trace. Keep them somewhat neat, but not sprawled out across the floor.

14) Don't tape cables to the floor. They become difficult to move or change in a hurry, plus tape leaves a residual sticky film on the cable and floor. In the control room and busier areas, such as doorways, lay a small rug over the cables. This keeps them in place and stops anyone from tripping over them. Next on the input/setup sheet are the microphone cables for the other guitar amplifiers.

15) The setup for guitar 1 has the head of the amplifier with the musician in the studio, and the bottom of the amplifier, or speaker cabinet, in isolation booth 1. This guitar setup also uses a direct box.

16) Connect the cables as you did for the bass guitar, with an XLR cable going from input 18 to the microphone stand in isolation booth 1. Then run another XLR cable going from input 19 to the direct box.

17) Again, connect one end of a ¼" cable to the input to the direct box, and leave the other end loose for the musician to connect his instrument. Run a second ¼" cable from the high impedance output of the direct box into the input of the amplifier. Connect the power cables for the amplifier. Leave the amplifier turned off.

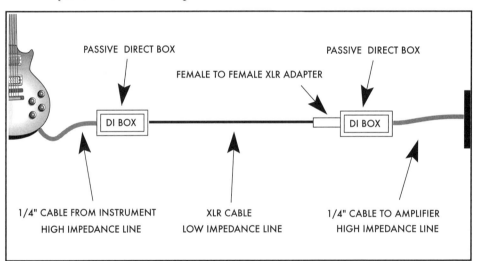

Figure 3.10 High Impedance Cable Extension

18) The setup for guitar 2, a combo amplifier, is in isolation booth 2. As there is no direct signal on this setup, no direct box is needed. Run a single cable from input 20 to the microphone stand in the isolation booth.

19) To run signal from guitar 2 all the way to the amplifier in isolation booth 1, one method is to run a long unbalanced ¼" cable. Because

unbalanced high impedance lines lose signal with increased length, you might consider another option.

Find two passive direct boxes, two ¼" cables, one long XLR cable, and a *same sex,* female-to-female XLR adapter. Plug one of the ¼" cables from the instrument into a direct box, changing the impedance of the signal from high to low. The *send* direct box can be either active or passive.

Run an XLR cable from the first direct box into the isolation booth, and into another passive direct box, using the female to female adapter. This then changes the signal back to high impedance. Plug out of the ¼" output of the direct box, and into the input of the amplifier (Figure 3.10). This combination will sound better than one long ¼" guitar cable.

20) The input/setup sheet shows that input 20 needs a -10dB in-line microphone pad. Figure 3.11 is an example of an in-line microphone pad. A pad lowers the incoming signal by a pre-determined level. Because the microphone being used lacks an internal pad, place the in-line pad between the microphone and the cable to reduce signal gain. In-line pads will interfere with a condenser microphone's phantom power. The "Shure SM-57" used on this amplifier is not a condenser microphone, but a dynamic microphone.

21) Next is on the input/setup sheet are the keyboards. Some keyboards have both XLR and ¼" outputs. Sometimes output levels must be changed to a more acceptable level using direct boxes. To save time, and to save direct boxes for other instruments, use the keyboards XLR output jacks.

22) If the keyboards are being recorded in stereo, label both ends of the cables as L and R and, if used, label both direct boxes as L and R. Any signal flow problems encountered can then be easily traced. Some engineers want the keyboards panned so the low notes are on the opposite of the low toms. For example, the low keys might be panned to the right if the low tom is panned to the left.

Figure 3.11 *In-line Microphone Pad*

23) According to the input/setup sheet keyboard 1 is connected to inputs 21 and 22, and keyboard 2 is connected to inputs 23 and 24. Because the keyboards do not use microphones, cables can be run from the output of the keyboards directly to the input panel.

24) Most keyboards don't use external amplifiers, therefore they can be plugged in and turned on without fear of blowing fuses.

25) After the keyboards are connected to the input panels, MIDI them together. According to the input/setup sheet, the master, which is keyboard 1, is MIDI'd to the slave, which is keyboard 2. Connect a MIDI cable from MIDI output on the master keyboard into MIDI input on the slave keyboard. Programmed MIDI instruments, such as drum machines, might stay in the control room, and connect to the console via the patchbay.

26) With the keyboards set up, the vocal and the talkback microphones are all that remain. A guide vocal track may be recorded with a basic track. This helps everyone in the studio and control room know where they are within the structure of the song at any given time, plus it keeps the flow of the song consistent. A guide vocal may even be used in part or in whole for the final vocal. There can be a certain magic that occurs when everyone is playing together in the studio, and watching each other.

When a singer is doing an overdub alone in the studio without the rest of the band, the music in the headphones may not elicit such an inspired performance.

27) Looking at the input/setup sheet, guitar player 2 will be singing the guide vocals. Run the cable for the guide vocal microphone to the vocal microphone stand from input 25.

28) The only cable left to be set up is for the talkback microphone. This is a centrally located microphone, used during larger sessions for the musicians to talk to the people in the control room, and to each other. Often the rest of the microphones in the studio are off axis with the musicians, so when they are talking with the people in the control room, or even with each other, no microphone picks up what they are saying. The talkback microphone will be whatever is left in the microphone closet.

29) Run this cable to the microphone stand from input 31, again according to the input/setup sheet.

After all amplifiers, instruments, cables, baffles, headphones and microphone stands are set up, the studio room is almost completely ready for the session. Now bring in the microphones.

MICROPHONES

Microphone care is a vastly important matter. Poorly maintained microphones simply will not endure as well as those that are properly looked after. While most equipment in the studio is sturdy enough to withstand the occasional mishandling, only the most durable microphones can weather such treatment. Many of the best and most popular microphones used in the studio today are decades old—proof that proper care and handling can yield high quality long term results.

Think of yourself as the engineer. Would you prefer old scratched and dented microphones that look as if they had been tossed around, or would you prefer pristine, well taken care of microphones? The answer seems obvious.

The changeable parameters on most microphones are basic, yet each microphone is different. Some microphones have no changeable parameters, others have switches on the outer casing. Some microphones have changeable heads for different in-line pads, different roll-offs (filters used to remove very low or high frequencies), and different polar patterns (grid patterns of a microphones response field, such as cardioid, omni-directional, bi-directional, or uni-directional). Contrary to popular belief, a polar pattern is not a weather front from Alaska.

Engineers unfamiliar with all of your studio's microphones will ask for details regarding their operation. Your job is to know the make and model of each of the studio's microphones, how many there are, and each microphone's primary application. As well, which are dynamic, condenser, or ribbon, along with each one's pad, roll-off, and polar patterns. Whenever the engineer's choice of microphones isn't available, you should be able to recommend a suitable substitute.

RETRIEVING MICROPHONES

The microphone room, or mic closet, is the home for all the microphones. Studios may keep the microphones in their original boxes, but realistically, after years of use these boxes get misplaced, lost, or discarded. Studios often store microphones on padded shelves in a dry cool room to keep them well protected.

The rest of the microphone supplies, such as microphone pads, clamps, shock mounts, windscreens, power supplies, and everything else associated with microphones are also stored here.

When bringing in the microphones—

• Carry one in each hand, even if many trips are necessary. Set up the microphones on one instrument at a time.

• Lay them out on a blanket on the floor or a table. Don't put them directly on the floor as they attract moisture and dust, and are easily stepped on or kicked about.

• Never put a tube microphone on a floor or table. Bring it out and immediately place it on the microphone stand. Tube microphones are too expensive and fragile to be placed anywhere but in their case, or on a microphone stand. Bring out the tube microphone's external power supply, and place it near the input panel. When the setup is complete, turn on the power supply. A tube microphone needs at least 30 minutes to warm up. Leave the power supply on for the rest of the session.

• Never put microphones on a bare piano as they may scratch the surface or worse, roll off and fall onto the floor. This gives a new meaning to the term "microphone roll-off."

CONNECTION MOUNTS

Microphones use two different kinds of mounts. One is the standard clip, or clutch, which grips the microphone to hold it in place. The other mount uses rubber bands or foam casings to isolate any vibrations from the stand and floor.

1) Be sure to use the same type of mount for both the microphones when recording in stereo. Don't put a shock mount on one, and a regular clip on the other.

2) Although mounts tend to get lost and broken, never use adhesive tape to modify microphones and mounts. Just get the correct mounts. With tape, the grip will loosen and the microphone may drop to the floor.

3) Always keep the mounts with their microphones—they are less likely to get lost.

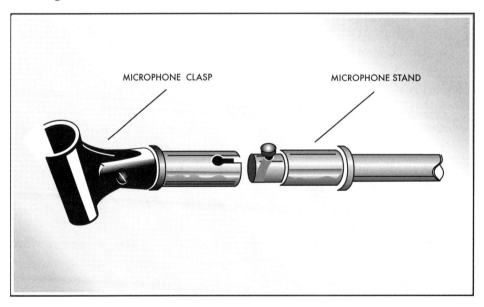

Figure 3.12 Quick-Lock Connectors

4) Quick-lock connectors are spring-loaded locks used to connect and dis-connect microphones quickly and easily from their stands. Figure 3.12. Without a quick-lock, the microphone must be screwed and unscrewed to the stand every time. If no quick locks are available, grasp the micro-phone and screw the stand to the microphone, rather than screwing the microphone to the stand. The other option is to remove the microphone from the mount, screw the mount on to the stand, and then re-connect the microphone to the mount.

MICROPHONE PLACEMENT

1) Starting with the bass guitar setup, bring out the correct microphone, as described on the input/setup sheet.

2) The bass guitar amplifier will be recorded with a Neumann U-47 tube microphone. Notice the engineer wants Neumann U-47 #2. Larger studios label their microphones of the same make and model, such as U-47 #1, #2, and #3. As individual microphones of the same make and model may each have slightly different characteristics, the engineer might request a specific microphone for vocals or for certain sensitive instruments. After working with all the studio's microphones, a good engineer will be able to hear slight differences in sound from one identical make and model to another.

3) Before placing the microphone in front of the bass amplifier, set any pads, roll-offs, or polar patterns according to the input/setup sheet. Setting the parameters is far easier when the microphone is still in your hand.

4) Connect the microphone to the stand that was previously placed, making sure the active side of the microphone is aiming toward the amplifier. Connect the cable resting on the stand to the microphone. The micro-phone is now connected to input 1.

5) As the bass guitar setup uses one microphone and one direct line, move on to setting up the microphones for the next instrument on the input/setup sheet—the drums.

6) Bring out and fasten all the drum microphones to their stands. Confirm that each microphone is firmly connected to the stand before connecting the cables. If a microphone drops off a stand during the session, everyone turns and looks at the assistant.

7) According to the input/setup sheet, two stereo pairs of microphones, inputs 14 to 17, are set up in opposite corners of the studio to record the ambiance of the drum kit. For this setup all amplifiers are isolated, so the only sound in the studio is the sound of the drums, with maybe some vocal leakage.

   Engineers sometimes like to record not only the close microphones on the drums, but distant microphones in the studio as well. This creates a certain ambient depth that simply cannot be re-created electronically. Engineers will want to try various microphone combinations to hear which ones sound best for different applications. They will choose the best ones and disregard the others. In this example, only one pair of ambient microphones would be used. Next on the input/setup sheet are the guitar amplifiers.

8) Place a Sennheiser 421 in front of the speaker cabinet in isolation booth 1, and a Shure SM-57 in front of the guitar amplifier in isolation booth 2. This is a common setup for guitars.

9) Run a ¼" speaker cable from the amplifier head in the studio, where the musician is located, to the speaker cabinet in isolation booth 1. This cable will usually come with the amplifier. After this setup, move on to the next item, the keyboards.

10) The keyboards need no microphones.

11) The vocal microphone uses a Neumann U-87, with a cardioid polar pattern setting.

12) Notice on the input/setup sheet that the only requirement for the talkback microphone is that it should be omni-directional. As most of the best microphones are probably already being used for the setup, use your judg-

ment and set up whatever microphone is left. An omni-directional pattern is needed to capture the whole studio. The engineer might record talkback microphones during the session. In this example, the talkback microphone is bussed to track 1.

13) When the engineer arrives for the session, he will fine tune the microphone placement.

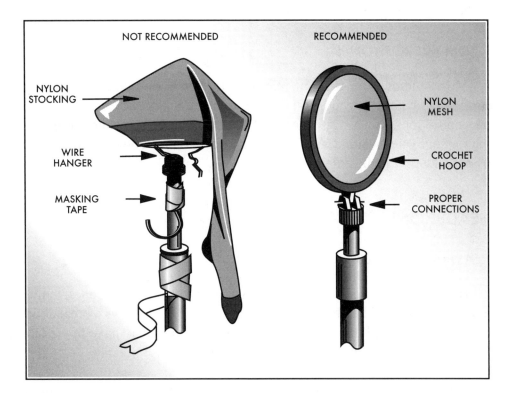

Figure 3.13 Pop Filters

POP FILTERS

A nylon pop filter, also called a windscreen, placed in front of a vocal microphone prevents most wind, or pop sounds. Pop filters, or windscreens such as Figure 3.13 are quite popular because they are easy to make, easy to set up, and very effective.

Lesser studios might use a nylon stocking wrapped around a bent wire coat hanger, and taped to a microphone stand. This is unprofessional, so replace this with a crochet hoop, a fresh nylon stocking, and a proper connection. Give the windscreen its own stand, unless there is a housing to hold it in place.

The old foam pop filters are still popular. There might be a small hole in front to be placed over the polar pattern indicator to see the pattern or pad without moving the pop filter.

ROOM MICROPHONES

Most studios have a room microphone that is permanently mounted somewhere within the studio, and accessible at the patchbay. The people in the control room can always hear what is happening in the studio, even if no microphones are apparent. Avoid voicing your dissatisfaction with the studio owner—he may be listening.

HEADPHONES

HEADPHONE BOXES

Headphone boxes split the cue signal to many sets of headphones, letting more than one musician hear the same mix. Figure 3.14 shows a breakdown of a standard headphone box. Some headphone boxes may have fewer features than this, some may have more. Most include—

- An input, used to receive a signal from the cue send. This is the main input into the headphone box, and is either ¼" or XLR.

- Volume controls.

- Stereo/mono switches. If additional cue sends are needed, there may be no other option but to use mono sends. To do this, the engineer might set up two separate mono cues from the left and right side of a stereo send. When the switch on the headphone box is on 1, the left side of the stereo cue is sending a mono signal to the headphones. When the switch is on 2, the right side of the stereo cue is sending a different mono signal to the headphones.

• Individual headphone outputs, either ¼" or XLR. During larger sessions, more than one set of headphones might be connected to one box.

• A through output by which an unaltered signal can be sent to additional headphone boxes in the studio.

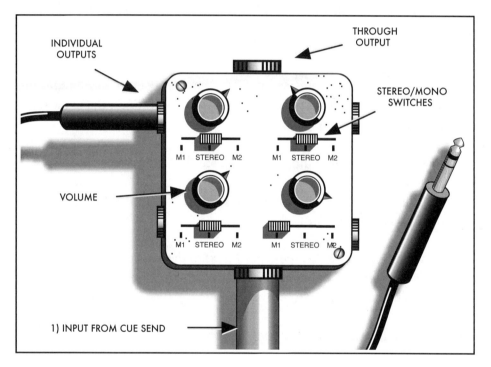

Figure 3.14 Headphone Box

CUE OPTIONS

There are many ways to send signal to the musicians' headphones. Musicians often need their own headphone mix, or cue mix, to hear exactly the right combination of instruments. When everyone shares one cue mix, each person invariably wants himself a little louder than everyone else.

Some studios have mini mixers for each cue station, so the musician has control over the level of each channel. If he wants to be louder in the cue mix, he simply reaches over and turns himself up. More common is the engineer doing separate cue mixes at the console.

According to the input/setup sheet, the drummer hears one cue mix, and the rest of the musicians hear another. Cue send 1 on the input panel feeds headphone boxes for the drummer. Cue send 2 on the input panel feeds the rest of the musicians. These cue sends might be normalled to mono or stereo sends on the console. (See Chapter Six for more on normals.)

HEADPHONES FOR THE PLAYERS

After getting the correct setup from the input/setup sheet regarding which musician gets what cue send, bring the headphones, the cables, and the headphone boxes into the studio.

1) Place the headphones throughout the studio for easy access.

2) Run the cables from the correct cue send output on the microphone input panel, into the headphone box.

3) Leave the excess cable on the floor next to the headphone box in case it needs to be moved. Keep the box and cable out of the way, leaving the musician enough room to move around.

4) Before plugging in any headphones, check that the cue amps are on.

5) Connect the headphones, checking that L and R on all headphones are working properly.

6) Set the headphones on a music stand or a chair, but never over the microphone stand, where they may feed back through the microphone. Don't leave the headphones on the floor.

7) Stash a spare set of headphones and a headphone box and cable set up off to one side. Sometimes headphones that work during setup will break down during the session. Having an extra setup ready will save time.

8) Some musicians may prefer a certain model of headphones. Use the same model headphones and box for him for the duration of the project. Once he is happy with his setup, stay with it.

HEADPHONES FOR THE ENGINEER

Place a set of headphones and a headphone box near the console for the engineer to use when setting up cue mixes. He will not want his headphones as loud as the musicians have theirs, so turn his headphone box down and unplug the headphones. Even the lowest of level coming out of a headphone in the control room can throw the engineer. He will plug them in when he needs to check the cue mixes.

Some consoles have a headphone output, but this is only useful if the engineer wants to hear the main monitor mix, not the individual cue mixes. Place the engineer's headphones away from the talkback microphone as they might feed back when he presses the talkback button.

HEADPHONES FOR THE ASSISTANT ENGINEER

You will also need a set of headphones with a long cord, not necessarily to hear the cue mixes, but to find sections of tracks, trim samples, set delay times, check returns, or to change settings on equipment.

As well, when the musicians see you wearing headphones, they think you are really getting into their music. With creative patching and headphones, you can do everything in relative silence while the rest of the room remains undisturbed. To set up the headphones—

1) Patch from the output of the unit being checked, into the input of a nearby CD burner or equivalent machine with an input setting.

2) Press the *record pause* button and monitor through the headphones.

3) Whenever you wear headphones, set the volume at a low level. Headphones can pump a lot of air pressure, which can easily damage eardrums.

Some musicians love to have the headphones obscenely loud, because of the impact. Think of the impact of being hit by a bus because you were too deaf to hear the driver honking the horn at you.

. . . .

Summary

Chapter Three explained how to retrieve and place cables, microphones and headphones for a session:

- Various signal levels, the decibel and impedance.

- The most common cables used in the studio, and their connection to the input panels.

- Different power sources for different applications.

- Using the input/setup sheet to correctly retrieve and place all microphones on their proper stands and connection mounts.

- Connecting the cables to the microphones, proper placement of all microphones, pop filters and direct boxes.

- Laying out all headphones and headphone boxes for the musicians and the engineer.

4

CHAPTER FOUR

· ·

Digital and Analog Recording Machines

The recording machines covered in this section include both digital and analog formats. Recording studios today record to either digital tape or, more commonly, the DAW—Digital Audio Workstation. The DAW is either a stand-alone unit, or a dedicated computer with applicable software and hardware.

Although the old 2" tape multitrack recorders are rapidly disappearing, analog recording is far from obsolete. Some engineers mix to analog tape because it can add a certain warmth. It is not uncommon to see engineers mix to analog and digital formats simultaneously. The client can hear both versions after mixing, then decide which to use.

You must understand the operation and parameters of whatever recording format the engineer chooses.

DIGITAL CONNECTIONS

Digital open reel machines, digital cassette machines and the DAW connect to any other digital device, such as a digital console or an external digital mixdown machine, without converting to analog. A single cable, such as light pipe or S/PDIF carries a digital data stream between devices, as long as the parameters match, and all devices read a common sync code. Among other connections, the digital machine should have analog ¼" or XLR inputs and outputs, just like an analog machine.

SESSION SHEET

The session sheet shows the artist, project number, song title, date, producer and engineers. It also details the preferred recording format and parameters, plus additional plug-ins. The engineer can arrive at the session with the confidence that his preferred recording system has been prepared to his specifications.

Figure 4.1 shows the session operating a DAW using WAV audio file type, with a 24 bit depth and a 48kHz sample rate. As well, the mix machine is an analog ½" tape machine with an alignment of $370nwb/m^2$.

DIGITAL AUDIO WORKSTATION

Ideally, the technical department will have connected the DAW in the studio. Let's assume all DAWs are turned on with the correct software and version. Your sessions will go faster if you have a firm grasp of all the keyboard shortcuts for your DAW. Lists of shortcuts are readily available in the workstation manual or on-line.

There are many different methods of setup, depending on the type of session, the studio, and the engineer's preference. There is no right or wrong way to set up, as long as it meets the needs of the session.

CREATE A MASTER

Create a *Master Session* folder wherein all *Master Sessions* will reside. Use the session setup sheet as your guide.

Artist ___The Tuff Beans_____ Project# ___631_____

Song ___Joe Perry's Guitar_____ Date ___August 06, Year___

Label ___Crapitol Records___ Contact _____ Phone ( ) _____

Producer ___Bob Loblaw_____ Phone ( ) _____

Engineer ___Casey Jones_____ Phone ( ) _____

Assistant Engineer ___A. Reader_____ Phone ( ) _____

ANALOG MACHINE INFORMATION

Analog Tape Machine(s) ___A-80___ Tracks ___1/2" 2 track___ Tape Speed ___30 ips___

Tones ___Reel 1___ Ref. Level 0VU = ___370 nwm___ Noise Reduction ___None___

Time Code Format	☐ 30	☐ 29.97 NDF	☐ 24	☐ SMPTE	Sync Ref (For master)
				☐ EBU	
	☐ 25	☐ 29.97 DF		☐ MTC	

DIGITAL MACHINE INFORMATION

Digital Machine _____ Tracks _____ Tape Speed _____

Bit Depth	☐ 16		Sample Rate	☐ 44.1 ☐ 88.2 ☐ 192
	☐ 24	Other _____		☐ 48 ☐ 96 ☐ Other _____

Time Code Format	☐ 30	☐ 29.97 NDF	☐ 24	☐ SMPTE	Sync Ref (For master)
				☐ EBU	
	☐ 25	☐ 29.97 DF		☐ MTC	

DAW INFORMATION

DAW Platform ☒ Mac ☐ PC ☐ Other | DAW Program ___Pro tools___

Host Computer ___Mac Jupiter___ Host Computer OS ___OX12.5___ Software Version ___23.5___

Bit Depth	☐ 16		Sample Rate	☐ 44.1 ☐ 88.2 ☐ 192
	☒ 24	Other _____		☒ 48 ☐ 96 ☐ Other _____

Time Code Format	☐ 30	☐ 29.97 NDF	☐ 24	☐ SMPTE	Sync Ref (For master)
				☐ EBU	
	☐ 25	☐ 29.97 DF		☐ MTC	

File Format ☐ BWAV ☐ AIFF ☒ WAV ☐ MP3 ☐ OTHER _____

Sync Source _____ Hard Disc _____ Notes _____

Plug ins _____

Figure 4.1 Session Sheet

- Check the date. Because every file is "time stamped" confirm that the computer's date and time are correct.

- Use the *setup* window to create a new session, name it *Master Session* and decide where it will be located—preferably in a new *Song Title—Master* file on its own hard drive. Set the file type, sample rate and bit depth, as well as any other settings, such as MAC/PC compatibility. WAV files are the preferred industry standard.

- Create the new tracks. Experience in the recording studio dictates that 16 tracks is a good starting point. Maybe create one track with the preferred plug-ins, then copy that track 15 times.

- With ease of moving channels around, common sense tells us to set the channels in the *mix* window to a standard placement. Standard layout of channels might be the drums, then guitars, vocals, and keyboards to the left of the master fader, and inputs or effects returns to the right. Of course in the *edit* window, the tracks wouldn't be on the left or right of the master fader, but above and below it.

- Use the input sheet, Figure 2.3 to set and label the inputs of each channel. Note, when labelling tracks, it is best not to use a "—" in the label, as this has been known to cause naming confusion within some DAW programs. Label the tracks before the recording begins.

- Assign the outputs as per the engineer's wishes. With today's surround sound, numerous outputs may need to be accessed.

- Assign the appropriate effects from the plug-ins window. Setting up limiters and compressors on each channel is fine, but understand that they affect the recorded signal only. The effect is not recorded unless the channel is bussed to another track, then recorded.

- Create a master fader.

- Set up the auxiliary sends, or aux. sends, simply called sends, and returns for the session. Depending on the session, you might start with a long plate, a short plate, and a delay.

- Clearly label the busses, inputs, outputs and inserts using the I/O settings window. For example, change "Interface 5, 6" to "Buss 5, 6 —> delay 1". Make use of a track's comments section for any additional comments.

- Start a tracksheet. (See Chapter Eight for more on tracksheets.)

- Rather than inserting effects such as chorus or reverb into individual audio tracks, insert effects into their own channels, accessible using properly labelled send and return routing.

- If applicable, create a MIDI channel and set up a click track channel.

- Set a color for each set of instruments, such as blue for drums, red for bass or yellow for vocals for visual reference.

- Once the file is complete and accurate, save this *Master Session* file in the *Master Session* folder. Clone this folder and rename it for the first song. *Song Title—Master* folder. Rename the session file within the folder *Song Title—Master* file.

  Ultimately, every song will have its own properly labelled master folder containing at least four items—the audio file folder, the fade file folder, the region file folder, and the correctly named master song file.

DIGITAL OPEN REEL

Open reel recording is rapidly disappearing in favor of the DAW, but some recording engineers still use digital multitrack tape recorders. If your session is, confirm that the multitrack machine is in placed in the correct location. Are the input meters clearly visible from the engineer's vantage point? Many recording studios have one large machine room, with each control room off it so each control room can access all available machines. To set up—

- Load the multitrack machine with a virgin tape.

- Set the machine's parameters, such as sample rate and bit depth as per the session sheet.

- As with analog tapes, exercise all digital tapes before use. (See later in this chapter for more on exercising the tapes.)

- Format any digital tapes by recording a control code from start to end of the tape (absolute time, also called A-time). Formatting is the process of recording a code on an internal code track. This code stores the digital information the machine needs to operate. The code allows, among other things, the machine to sync with another digital device, and it lets the user see exactly where the tape is located at any given time.

- If time allows, format the tapes before the session starts, because once the formatting starts, the tape should run through to the end uninterrupted.

- Wind the reel to the top of the tape, then switch the appropriate tracks into *record-ready*.

ANALOG MIXDOWN MACHINE

The analog machine for our reference will be a $1/2''$ 2 track machine. The traditional 16 or 24 track 2'' analog tape machines are still in demand in some circles, but have been vastly overshadowed by today's digital multitrack recording systems. All connections, cleaning, demagnetizing and aligning that is detailed here is applicable to any size machine, including 2'' analog tape machines.

Again, confirm that the machine is in the correct location. Note that moving analog machines any distance may slightly change the alignment. You should check the bias and alignment after such a move. (See later in this chapter for more on alignment procedures.)

ANALOG CONNECTIONS

All mixdown machines have an input section and an output audio section. This is where the individual tracks are recorded and played back. The term "track" refers to the capacity of the mixdown machine, and the term "channel" refers the modules on the console. For example, the mixdown machine has 2 tracks, and the console has 56 channels.

The standard inputs and outputs to professional open reel analog machines use XLR balanced cables to send and receive audio. These machines also have non-audio ports, including connections to external transport, timecode and video sync tracks, track remote, and auto-locator remote. DL, or EDAC multi-pair connectors connect the console to the machine via a single port that houses all inputs and outputs.

FRONT OF THE MACHINE

If you are unfamiliar with anything to do with the workings of the machines, ask someone who knows. Of course, wait for an appropriate time to ask. When the engineer is deep in concentration during a difficult session, don't jump in and say "Geez, I wonder what happens if I press this itty bitty button here?" Do not press a button, flip a switch, pull a cable, or turn a knob while the transport is in motion. And if you do not know what something does, leave it alone. Learn the equipment through daily use, lots of reading, questioning engineers, and sneaking into the studio at 3 a.m.

CLEANING

Due to daily use, studio gear tends to get covered in pencil marks, grease smudges, pieces of tape, dust, and general studio grime, so the machines occasionally need cleaning. This will not involve any drastic measures, so power hoses and rubber boots will not be necessary. A simple pencil eraser will remove most of the marks, but sometimes a tissue with alcohol is needed. For best results—

- Clean the analog tape heads before a session.

- Dip one or two cotton swabs into a bottle of isopropyl alcohol—never rubbing alcohol. Shake off the excess alcohol, and then run the swab over the non-rubber surfaces of the tape path, starting with the heads. Start at one edge and swipe the swab over the head a few times to clean the full area of the head. Do this gently to avoid damaging the head. Remember, clean your head, don't scratch it.

- Clean the rubber rollers along the tape path with cotton swabs dipped in soapy water (not alcohol, which dries out rubber.) Clean the rollers on both analog and digital open reel machines.

- As some machines run continually during a session, the oxide from the analog tape sheds onto the heads and rollers. The oxide residue needs to be cleaned regularly, approximately every six hours. Do this during the session when the machine won't be in use for a few moments, whether you are asked to or not.

- Wait until the machine will not be in use for a few minutes. Lower the head protector, then unwind the tape from the front of the heads, keeping the tape well away from any stray droplets of alcohol.

• Wait until the alcohol has evaporated, then tighten the tape on both spindles, return the head protector, and press the stop button to activate the machine's mechanics.

DEMAGNETIZING

The heads and rollers along the analog tape path periodically become magnetized from being in constant contact with the tape, and must be demagnetized with a demagnetizer. Once before the session is enough. Switch the multitrack machine off before demagnetizing. To demagnetize the heads—

1) Remove all tapes from the vicinity—imagine what a device called a demagnetizer could do to an audio tape!

2) Turn on the de-magnetizer and hold it at least three feet (one meter) away from the heads.

3) Slowly bring it in and run it up and down the heads, not quite touching. Go over the heads two or three times, then demagnetize the non-rubber rollers, capstans, and all contact points along the tape path that may retain magnetism.

4) Slowly bring it away from the heads until it is again about one meter away. Switch the demagnetizer off and remove it from the room.

Confirm that all the cables are properly connected, that the machine parameters are correct, and that the master gain on the console is muted. Then switch on the machine. Report any meters that have burned out lights, or that are not reacting correctly. As well, note any lights on the console that are loose or burnt out.

Let the machine warm up for at least 30 minutes before checking the alignment. Check all tape machines for correct alignment before each session, and align if necessary.

HEADS, TAILS AND PRE-PRINT THROUGH

When an analog tape is packed heads out on a reel, pre-print through may occur. This happens when recorded signal transfers from one layer of tape on a reel to an adjacent layer. When analog tapes are stored heads out, pre-print through may be heard before a song starts. When tapes are stored tails out, pre-print through would not occur until after the song starts, so it wouldn't normally be heard. Digital reels are stored heads out.

ALIGNMENTS

Professional analog tape recorder heads are aligned to adjust for correct input and output level for reliable frequency response. Industry wide standards for aligning tape machines ensure that if a tape recorded at one studio is taken to another studio, the *record* and *playback* levels match.

Professional multitrack analog heads have three alignable sections. The *repro* section, sometimes called *playback* or *output*, the *sync* section, and the *record* section, sometimes called the *cue*. More technical alignments, such as the azimuth (the perpendicular angle of the head) are occasionally checked by the technical staff.

Once the heads are aligned for a specific project, reference tones are recorded, usually on reel 1 or the designated tone reel. These tones are then used for alignments during the rest of the project.

In larger studios, the technical staff is responsible for machine alignments. Ultimately, the assistant is responsible for making sure alignments are correct and complete. Unlike analog machines, digital recording and playback levels are set and unchangeable.

LEVELS

Commercially available pre-recorded tone reels are used to align professional analog machines. These tone reel tapes contain, among other tones, 1kHz, 10kHz, and 100Hz tones recorded at an industry standard operating level of 0dB, which can be any reference level determined by the manufacturer.

Alignment tones are recorded using a nwb/m^2 (NanoWebers per meter squared) fluxivity standard. For example, one company may produce alignment tapes with tones recorded at 0dB = 250nwb/m^2. When this tape is played, the user adjusts the playback level on each channel to zero on the VU meters, aligning the heads to 0VU= 250nwb/m^2.

Figure 4.2 shows how aligning machines to +3 over the 0VU standard results in an alignment of 0VU= 370nwb/m^2, and +6dB over the 250nwb/m^2 standard, results in an alignment of 0VU= 510nwb/m^2. Note that these numbers are not to exact standards. (See Chapter Three for more on how an increase of 6dB doubles the level.)

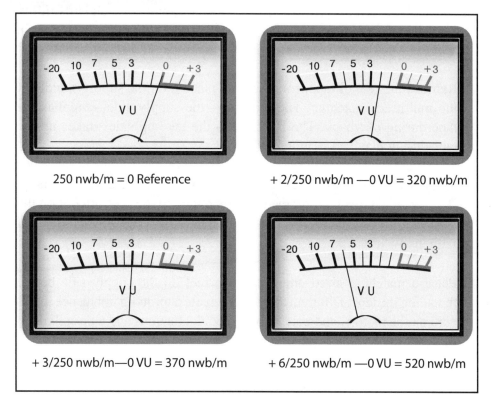

Figure 4.2 *NanoWebers/VU*

Advancements in tape technology allow elevated recording levels due to increased headroom. This means that today's analog tapes can withstand hotter signal before saturation. If the engineer wants the alignment levels elevated by 3dB to 370nwb/m, align the meter levels to -3VU. This then requires an additional 3dB to bring signal up to 0VU.

Before starting the alignment, understand exactly what you are doing. When the machine is incorrectly aligned, problems may not be immediately apparent. Level differences will definitely be noticed when the machine is correctly aligned for your next session.

LOAD THE TONE REEL

Begin the playback alignment by loading the tone reel on the machine. European (IEC), and North American (NAB) alignment standards differ. There are many fine books available that explain all about the differences in equalization standards. This ain't one of 'em. To begin the alignment—

1) Remove the reel of tape from the box, place it on the supply spindle of the multitrack machine. The left side—the supply side—supplies the tape during playback. The right side—the take-up side—takes up the tape during playback. Tighten the locks.

2) Remove any collar holding the end of the tape in place, and set it nearby. If adhesive tape is holding the end of the tape to the reel, stick it on the corner of the multitrack machine so you can use it again when finished with the reel.

3) Place a matching sized empty take-up reel on the supply side before threading the tape. Different sized reels create a torquing imbalance that is hard on the motors, and may cause speed fluctuations and tape spillage.

4) Guide the tail end of the tape through the tape path, across the heads, and through the capstan rollers to the empty supply side.

5) Splice off the very end bit of tape if it is wrinkled or torn at all. The empty reel will grasp the end section of tape much better if the tape is clean and wrinkle free.

6) Replace the head protector after threading to avoid hum.

7) Retrace the tape path, checking that it is correct before engaging the transport of the machine. If the tape is re-wound while threaded wrong, you risk damaging 1) the machine, 2) the tape, 3) your credibility.

8) Check to see if the empty reel is bent, as the tape may rub against the inside. When this happens, remove the reel, and turn it over. If the rub remains, replace the empty reel with another one.

9) Wind the alignment tape to the section containing 1kHz and park it there. The machine is now ready for the playback alignment.

PLAYBACK ALIGNMENT

Confirm that the VSO, the variable speed oscillator, and noise reduction are switched off, then find the correct alignment tool and begin. Alignment pots in the machines can sometimes get dirty, and must be cleaned. Do this by inserting the alignment tool and gently but liberally working the alignment pots back and forth. Remember, occasionally clean the pots in the sync! In this example, our alignment tones are recorded at $0VU = 250nwb/m^2$.

1) Start with the *repro* section, then do the *sync* section, and finally the *record* section. Switch the machine to *repro* and lower the main monitors. Understand that tones don't need to be loud to be heard.

2) Mute all master sends. Tones will be sent to the inputs of any outboard equipment normalled from any sends that happen to be turned up. As well, the cue sends to headphones must be switched off, or else the tones may blast out the elements. Either turn them down, or deadpatch the cue sends at the patchbay. (See Chapter Six for more on deadpatching.)

3) The alignment tape is parked at the spot that begins the 1kHz tone. This tone is used to set the overall output level. Some recording studios might use a reference of 700Hz for the level alignment. Figure 4.1 shows the analog mix machine needs to be aligned to 0VU= 370nwb/m^2. Play the alignment tape and adjust the repro level alignment pot for all tracks to -3VU. Figure 4.2 shows that when the alignment is set at -3dB, the incoming signal must be 3dB louder to reach 0VU.

4) When the *repro* level alignment is completed on all tracks, transport the alignment tape to the section that holds 10kHz and do the same alignment on the *repro* section high-frequency pots.

5) Because these tones are recorded as one track across the width of the tape, a $^1/_2''$ tone reel can be used to align $^1/_2''$ 2-track or 4-track machines. This full track across the width of the tape creates a low frequency effect known as fringing, occurring when the heads draw low frequency signal from outside the normal tape path, giving an inaccurate reading on the meters. The low end *repro* alignment will be done during the record alignment.

6) After aligning the *repro* high frequency alignment, transport the tape back to the 1kHz section of the alignment tape.

7) Change the operating status, or mode of the multitrack machine to *sync* and re-do the same level and high frequency alignment procedure, adjusting the *sync* pots.

8) When *repro* and *sync* are aligned, transport the alignment tape off, and replace the collar on the tone reel. When no collar is available, use the small strip of adhesive tape mentioned earlier.

9) Remove the tone reel from the machine and put it away. Because you will usually make and use only one tone reel for a project, the commercial tone reel will not be used for the rest of the project.

REMOVING A REEL/PACKING

When you rewind or fast-forward a tape on a reel, the high speeds can cause it to pack unevenly, leaving the outside edges exposed, perhaps losing the integrity of the edge tracks. When tapes are played off, or slow wound to the end of the reel, they pack smoothly and evenly. Digital tapes aren't susceptible to this uneven packing, and can be wound without worry of exposed edges.

Some analog machines have a slow wind feature, allowing the tape to pack evenly as it winds off. Some machines also have an auto torquing feature that slows the transport down when nearing the end of the reel.

When you are quickly changing reels during a busy mix session, there may be little time to slow-wind the reel off. Fast-forward the reel off. Later, when you have enough time, re-load the tape, rewind it to the beginning of last song worked on, and slow-wind it off, making sure the packing is smooth and uniform. If a second machine is available, you can do this during the session.

All tapes destined for long-term storage must be slow-wound and packed smoothly. Whether rewinding or fast-forwarding, avoid letting any reel go so fast that it whips off the end of the reel loudly flapping until it finally stops. No one wants to see their tapes mishandled.

RECORD ALIGNMENT

LOADING AND EXERCISING

Remove a virgin analog reel from the box, take it out of the plastic bag, and set the tape upside down on the take-up side spindle of the mixdown machine. This reel will be dedicated as the tone reel and used for the record alignment.

This is usually Reel 1 of many and will hold the tones and the *record pad*—a section of tape used for doing a daily record alignment. Eventually, these tones will be moved to Reel 1 of the master reels. This reel should be the same brand, model number and batch as the rest of the reels used for the project. For consistency of sound quality, try to stay within a batch throughout the project. Remove the sticker with the batch number from the end of the reel, and stick it inside the tape box. This sticker must be kept for reference in case any problems arise with the tape or batch of tapes.

Exercise the virgin tape before first use. This doesn't mean taking the tape out for a stroll around the lake, it means to align the packing, or tension of a virgin tape with the torque of the machine. To exercise the tape—

1) With the virgin reel upside down on the take-up side of the mixdown machine, place an empty reel on the supply side.

2) Thread the tape, re-zero the tape counter, then wind the reel to the end.

3) With all the tape now on the supply side, re-thread the tape into the take-up side. The beginning of the tape may retain some residual magnetism left by the large blade used at the tape factory. Splice off the first few feet of tape at the beginning and splice in a foot or two of leader. A leader is a strip of paper or plastic inserted between separate sections of tape to keep track of all sections.

The reel of tape should now be at to the beginning and ready for the record alignment.

If a client arrives with a single virgin reel, load the reel upside down on the take-up side of the machine, thread it, and rewind it all the way off to supply side reel. Turn the now empty original reel over, and re-thread the tape. When the session ends, the client's tape will be tails out, packed evenly, and on his original reel.

OSCILLATOR

Professional consoles have a built-in oscillator (a pure sine wave generator with a gain control and a full range of frequencies) accessible in the patchbay. The oscillator is used, among other things, to align the tape machines, to test signal flow, to set unity gain, to trace down problems and, if loud enough, to eject bothersome record producers from the control room.

BIAS

Begin the record alignment with the biasing. Bias, a very high-frequency tone somewhere close to 150kHz is recorded with the audio signal to help it bond to the tape.

Have you ever had anything engraved, such as a little tin heart on a little tin chain that says "To Mila, From Tim"? I have. An electric engraving pencil's tip vibrates so fast that it digs right into the tin. Without that high frequency vibration, the tip of the engraving pen would only scratch the surface of the tin. This concept is the general principle behind tape biasing. The high-frequency tone recorded with the audio signal vastly increases the tape retention.

1) To set bias, switch on the console oscillator. Studios use either 10kHz, 15kHz or 1kHz as the carrier frequency to set bias. Whatever is standard where you work is the right way.

2) For this application, switch the machine to *repro* mode, with all tracks in *record-ready*.

3) Record the tone on all tracks.

4) Some machines have a bias pot for each track, and some machines have a single bias pot for the entire machine. As you record, turn the bias pot all the way down (counter-clockwise) then slowly bring it up, watching the meters. The needle will rise past zero and into the red, reach its highest point, then descend again.

5) Continue turning clockwise, allowing the needle to descend from 1 to 4dB from the highest point on the VU meter, depending on the tape used and the studio overbias standard. This overbiasing has proven to increase sound quality.

6) Now begin the record alignment.

RECORDING TONES

To begin the record alignment, rewind to where the alignment tones will be recorded, usually after the first leader on the as-yet unrecorded tone reel.

1) Set the oscillator at 1kHz and leave all tracks on the machine in *record-ready*. Switch the multitrack machine to *auto-input*. Auto-input mode switches the machine to input when it is not in motion. This should put all tracks on the multitrack machine in *input*.

2) Adjust the output level of the oscillator to 0VU on the meters of the machine.

3) With the machine in *repro*, press *play* and *record*, then adjust the *record* level alignment pot to 0VU on all tracks. As you adjust this pot, monitor the *repro* level, which is aligned correctly because you just did it. When the *record* level reaches 0VU, the *record* input level matches the *repro* output level.

4) After the *record* level is aligned on all tracks, change frequencies on the oscillator to 10kHz.

5) Adjust the *record* high frequency pots to 0VU.

6) Change the oscillator to low frequency, either 50Hz or 100Hz and continue recording while adjusting the *repro* level of those low frequencies.

7) After completing the alignment, mark a corner of the machine with the alignment level, tape speed, the brand and model number of tape the machine was biased for, the project, the date, and your name. This information is included in case someone wants to question or comment on the alignment.

CREATE A TONE REEL

After completing the record alignment, go to the beginning of the tone reel. Record at least 30 seconds each of 1kHz, 10kHz, 15kHz, 100Hz, and 50Hz. After these tones, install at least a two-minute section of *record* pad. These tones and pad are then leadered, clearly labeled, and used for all future alignments on this project. These tones might go on Reel 1.

AFTER THE ALIGNMENT

After the alignment is complete, load the session reel, and transport it to the correct spot. If the reel is virgin, exercise it, then wind to the beginning of the reel. If the reel is not virgin, go to the end of the last song on tape. Confirm there is enough tape for a complete pass. Switch the tracks to *record-ready*. The machine is now ready for recording.

CHECK EACH REEL

As *record* levels to tape may vary slightly from reel to reel, even within a batch, some engineers want each virgin analog reel tested before use. Sessions can go through many reels, so checking the record alignment for each reel must be fast. To check the alignment for each reel—

1) Do so only when the musicians have removed their headphones or, more advisable, after the signal has been muted in the cue sends, turn on the oscillator.

2) After loading and exercising the virgin reel, quickly record a small amount of 1kHz, 10kHz, and 100Hz at the start of the tape. If the *sync* and *repro* levels coming back aren't consistent with the alignment, or if the tones are waving when they shouldn't be, bring it to the engineer's attention. He will of course want to use a different reel, or maybe even a different batch.

3) Splice off the section of tape used for the tones, as they tend not to erase totally when recorded over.

Don't let anyone in the session hear alignment tones, or tone from the oscillator. If you are alone in the control room, use the speakers to check tones. However if a client is there, use headphones. If you must use speakers, keep the gain low, because anyone in the recording industry knows that a good loud blast of 10,000Hz hurts.

. . . .

Summary

Chapter Four explained how to handle digital and analog tapes and machines for a session:

- Placement of the machines for optimum use.

- Bringing all the tapes and media into the studio.

- Creating master DAW files.

- Cleaning, demagnetizing and aligning of the tape machines.

- Creating a tone reel for alignments on your project.

CHAPTER FIVE

. . . .

Outboard and Speakers

OUTBOARD EQUIPMENT

In the recording studio, the outboard equipment includes all external processing devices not housed within the console or DAW. These various pieces of outboard equipment, such as equalizers, limiters, delays, samplers, echo plates and reverbs are used when additional signal processing is needed, either for recording, mixing or monitoring.

You are expected to know what outboard equipment the studio has, how to access all settings, store custom programs and, most importantly, how to explain it all to the engineer. If necessary, choose a section in your daily log with a few reminders or tips on operating unfamiliar equipment. (See Chapter Seven for more on daily log.)

Whenever new equipment arrives, the accompanying manuals are quite helpful. They keep the engineer busy while you get in there and learn how the new equipment works. When clients are paying massive amounts of money to rent a studio and hire a big gun engineer, they don't want to be waiting around because no one knows how to use the new piece of outboard.

STANDARD OUTBOARD RACKS

Most studios have stationary racks that contain the standard outboard equipment. These racks always stay in the control room and are located where the engineer can easily reach the controls. The equipment is usually hard-wired to the patchbay, and is included in the base rate of the studio.

Engineers expect the studio to supply a reasonable amount of outboard equipment. A piece of outboard equipment might be removed from the control room when it's being held for another session, or because it's malfunctioning. The studio will usually supply a comparable substitute. If any standard outboard has been pulled, find out why before your session begins.

ADDITIONAL OUTBOARD

When the engineer needs additional outboard equipment for the session, it will usually be rented from the studio or from a local equipment rental company, usually at additional cost to the client. Keep a current list of the studio's rental equipment, sometimes called floaters, and equipment available from local rental companies.

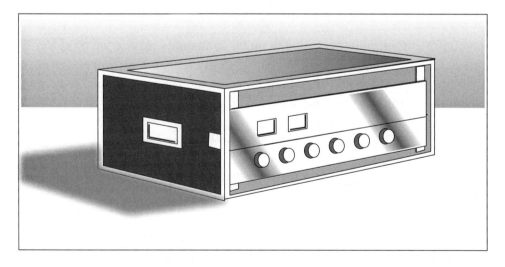

Figure 5.1 Standard Outboard Rack

Outboard equipment not permanently mounted in stationary racks are usually housed in standard 19-inch-wide road cases for protection while in transit, and for ease of stacking. Figure 5.1 shows that these cases usually leave an inch or two at top and bottom of the case, and sometimes have a small fan to keep the equipment cool. The equipment stays in the case, and the front and back panels are removed to access the controls and connections. The proper cables and power cords are included.

Sometimes the engineer may bring his own rack of outboard, all programmed with his favorite settings. This is not only convenient for the engineer, but usually cheaper for the client than renting additional outboard for the duration of a project. Some of these racks are set up with power strips and mini patchbays, making setup even easier.

RENTING EQUIPMENT

For some sessions, additional outboard equipment microphones, cables, stands, or modules must be rented. Audio rental companies have almost all equipment available today and, in major cities. Keep lists of audio equipment rental companies and telephone numbers of neighboring studios in case anything needs to be rented or borrowed.

Before ordering items from the rental companies, advise the producer to prevent unforeseen problems. When the equipment arrives, you or someone will need to sign for it. Verify that the serial numbers on the invoice correspond to equipment received, and that all manuals and cables are included. Make a note of any scratches or dents.

PLACEMENT AND CONNECTION

Whether the additional equipment being used is the engineer's own equipment, a floater, or a rental, it needs to be correctly placed in the control room. Before bringing the equipment into the control room, make a space where the engineer can comfortably reach the settings. Most studios have space for outboard cases to be placed next to the console, or behind the engineer. If an equalizer is half way across the control room, and off to one side, the engineer must move out of the main sound field area, and may not be able to hear the slight changes being made. To set up this additional outboard equipment—

- Bring the cases containing the outboard equipment into the control room, and remove the front and back panels before stacking them. You don't want to stack them up, only to find the bottom one is upside down. As you remove the panels, label them with the name of the unit from which they were removed, and whether they are front or back panels.

- When the rental is for an extended project, the engineer may want the units placed within the stationary rack. If the equipment is rented only for a few days, the front and back panels may be put in studio storage, rather than left in the control room.

- When many cases are brought in, don't stack them too high on top of each other. This may create a sound block and change the acoustics of one side of the audio spectrum. Also, it is very easy to bump into an unstable stack of these expensive and delicate items, creating a veritable "Fourth of July" when they come crashing down with sparks flying and black smoke everywhere. It's even more enjoyable when someone else does it.

POWER UP/POWER DOWN

Many pieces of equipment may be plugged in at one small area where all the outlets are, so use care when plugging or unplugging power. Accidentally unplugging the power cord of an active piece of outboard equipment might not be an issue at the beginning of a session, but may cause problems toward the end of a session, especially a mixdown session. Not all equipment retains specific settings during power down, so settings will be lost unless they were stored, either internally or on a setup sheet. If the unit is active in the monitors when powering up or down, mute the returns on the console to avoid a great pop. This pop usually blows speakers, fuses, and minds.

99

Most pieces of equipment have a removable power cable. Before connecting the power cable to the equipment, label it at the plug end with the name of the equipment it connects to. This ensures its proper return. You will be glad you did when you are crawling around trying to find an open outlet, or tracing a power cable to find where it originates. If you make a habit of keeping the proper cord with the proper unit, you will never lose the cord—unless, of course, you lose the entire unit.

BACK PANEL

Sometimes outboard equipment not connected to the bay has to be accessed at the back of the piece of equipment itself. This means crawling behind the outboard rack, cables in hand, whenever the engineer decides he wants a change. Depending on his needs, you may have to connect the equipment to the patchbay, or to other outboard.

Connecting different pieces of outboard equipment can be challenging, since different equipment manufacturers sometimes use different input and output formats, with assorted wiring combinations. Most professional outboard equipment has either XLR or $^1/_4$" connections, and both may have different pin wiring configurations. The technical staff might need to create special cables with various connectors at both ends to accommodate all connections. If you can, use the balanced XLR connections. Most outboard equipment has one or two inputs, and two or four outputs. Some have more, and all will be labeled with their proper function.

Before connecting the unit, ask the engineer which inputs and outputs he prefers. Tell him if there is any additional level or equalization controls on the back panel that he might not know about. If he is not there to ask, connect the unit as you see fit, and check with him when he arrives.

CONNECTIONS

Outboard equipment that always stays in the control room is usually accessed at the patchbay. Some studios label the patchbay, showing where all the outboard appears. Other studios label the individual pieces of outboard equipment with the corresponding patch point numbers at the bay. Others keep a list next to the console showing each piece of outboard equipment, and its corresponding patch point numbers. When the engineer needs a certain piece of equipment, you can look at the numbers on the list, find the corresponding patch points in the patchbay, and make the patch. (See Chapter Six for more on patching.)

Many studios have input panels in the control room that are wired directly to the patchbay. When additional outboard equipment is brought in, connect it to the patchbay through these input panels via short XLR cables. Either label the new piece of outboard equipment with its patch point numbers, or add the numbers to the current outboard list.

TESTING SIGNAL FLOW

Once a piece of additional outboard is placed, connected and turned on, double check the inputs and outputs, the sends and returns from the console, and the left/right integrity. The left cable must be on the left side, and the right cable must be on the right side. Connect the outboard equipment properly before the engineer tries to use it and finds out it isn't working. Listen to the returns to see if the unit is correctly grounded. Occasionally, if a unit has a buzz or hum, it needs to be grounded.

Use the oscillator to trace the signal path to check that everything is properly connected. We will delve deeper into the patchbay later, but for now, do these few simple patches. Some engineers want you to set the input and output levels at unity gain using the oscillator.

UNITY GAIN

Unity gain is simply the equipment's input level matching its output level. To set unity gain, patch out of the oscillator, and into a nearby input meter. The meters on the multitrack should be close and convenient. Set the oscillator output level at 0VU according to the meter on the machine. Patch out of the oscillator and into the piece of outboard then back into the input meter on the machine. Set the input levels and output levels of the outboard to read 0VU.

You may also want to check that 0VU on the channel fader is actually 0VU on the console channel meters. This works for limiters, equalizers and delays, but a pure tone into echo plates or reverbs may not give an accurate reading, so if possible, use white noise to set the levels. (See later in this chapter for more on white noise.)

RESET

Most units have a reset button to be pressed when the unit freezes. This button, surprisingly enough, resets the unit to its original factory specifications, losing all the stored programs that you and everyone else have so painstakingly created. If the unit needs resetting, first try turning it off and then on. As a last resort, press the reset button. Of course, mute the returns before doing this.

STUDIO TIE LINES

Many recording studios have more than one control room, and each control room must keep adequate outboard equipment for sessions to proceed. Invariably, when working in one control room, the engineer also wants to use equipment from the other control room. One option is to remove the outboard from the other studio, bring it in, and set it up for your session. Check with the studio manager before removing any equipment from another control room. Even if the other room is not in use, another session may be scheduled to start before your session ends.

Another option is to connect equipment in another control room through tie lines. Tie lines link all the patchbays within a premises, so that all equipment can be accessed from any room. All equipment can theoretically stay where it is, and be used for any session in any control room. Of course, someone has to go to the other control room to make the patches and set the levels—usually you. Larger equipment, such as an echo plate, might be kept in a distant closet and connected through tie lines.

CLICK GENERATORS

A click may be sent through the cue mix to help the musicians keep the timing of each song consistent through all takes. Without it, slight tempo changes may occur from the first take to the last. Some players are opposed to playing along to a rigid time structure, and prefer to let the natural flow of the music guide the tempo.

A click can be generated by anything from a microphone on a metronome to a complete set of electronic drums, to a click generated by a digital recording and editing system. Unlike most outboard equipment, click generators don't have an audio input. They can be driven by other codes, but it's not a send and return situation. A click generator is also used to help the engineer edit the multitrack tape from one take to another.

Operation and setup of click can get complicated, as there may be timecode that goes with the click to drive a sequencer.

To set up an external click, either patch directly out of the click generator into the multitrack or bring it up in a channel on the console, and assign it to the multitrack. The click track is sent to the musicians through the cue sends, the same as any other track.

One of the players, commonly the drummer has the click generator with him in the studio, or the click may be in the control room. However it is set up, the engineer must set the *record* level, and the cue mix level to headphones. If the click generator is in the control room, you may have to start and stop the click generators, as the engineer has more important things to do. Label the tracksheet with the correct BPM (beats per minute.)

Whenever recording a click to analog tape, set the level low, around -10dB as the high transients might leak into neighboring tracks, wreaking havoc on adjacent timecode tracks. If you find high transients leaking in your studio, talk to the manager about beefing up security.

VIDEO

Some studios are laid out in such a way that the control room can't be seen from the studio, so video cameras sometimes link the control room and the studio. Place the camera where the control room can monitor the widest area of the studio. Place the video monitor at an appropriate spot in the control room, such as between the stereo speakers in front of the console.

Video is not always used simply to monitor the studio activities. For movie and television soundtracks and jingle sessions, the audio being recorded is synchronized to a pre-recorded video. As the musicians watch the video monitor, they play along with it. The music is then synchronized with the video. This lets the producer see and hear how the audio and video work together. Animators and music video makers tend to do the opposite, making the video after the audio is recorded.

SPEAKERS

The term *monitor* normally refers to the complete unit, and the term *speaker* normally refers to the actual cone. The main monitors in most control rooms are a pair of large permanently mounted studio monitors aimed at the center of the console where the engineer sits. All control rooms have at least one set of studio near field "bookshelf" monitors sitting on the console at ear level.

These are often referred to as the big speakers and the small speakers, or simply upstairs and downstairs. Many engineers get used to a certain make and model of bookshelf speaker, and always use that particular one in the studio. They either bring their own, or specify to the studio which ones to have available for the session.

SPEAKER REMOVAL AND REPLACEMENT

Sometimes, speakers in the control room need replacing. If the studio owns additional small speakers, matching replacement speakers should be somewhere on the premises. Don't remove a speaker from another control room without authorization. Sometimes it may be best to replace both speakers of a matched set, rather than just replacing one. To replace or add speakers for the session—

1) Remove all tapes from the vicinity before bringing any speakers into the control room. Speakers have magnets and magnets erase tapes.

2) Mute the gain on the console. Some studios even have you turn off the amplifiers before disconnecting speakers.

3) If replacing the present speakers, unhook the wires, noting which wires were on which terminal.

4) If the grilles (the protective cloth covers on the front of the speakers) have been removed, find them and fasten them to the front of the speaker casing. Remove the speakers and place them on the floor next to the console. Face them inward, toward each other, so the cones won't accidentally get kicked in.

5) Bring in the replacement speakers. Remove them from their cases if necessary, and set them where the old ones were. If you are not replacing the speakers, but simply adding additional speakers, set them on matching stands close to the existing ones. There should be additional cables from a second amplifier to connect to these speakers.

6) Place the speakers so the tweeters face out or up. Some engineers will want the grilles removed.

7) Connect the cables to the back of the speakers, making sure the phase is correct, and the left cable is on the left speaker, and the right cable is on

the right speaker. Correct phase occurs when the grounding wire within each cable is connected to the same post on both speakers.

8) Sit in the engineer's chair and check for proper speaker placement. Figure 5.2 shows a triangle between the speakers and the listener.

9) All speakers should have fuses installed so that a power surge will blow the fuse before the speaker. If the speaker is fatigued, the fuse may not protect it from blowing. At times, the engineer will monitor loud enough to blow a speaker, or a power surge on the line will move so fast that both the fuse and the speaker will blow simultaneously. However, some recording engineers feel that fuses change the sound of the speaker, and do not use them. They monitor at their own risk. If the engineer blows an expensive speaker, the studio manager may have a power surge.

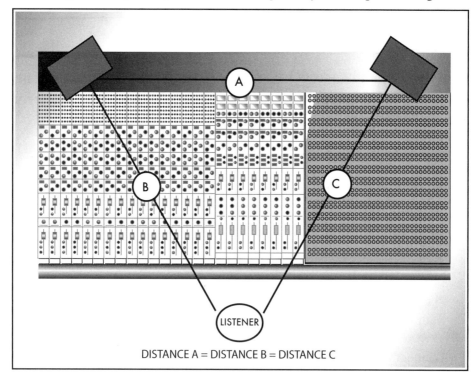

DISTANCE A = DISTANCE B = DISTANCE C

Figure 5.2 Proper Speaker Placement

10) Turn the amplifiers on and listen to a familiar song to check that the speakers are working and properly connected. Listen to the high, mid, and low frequencies to confirm the speakers are working correctly on both sides, if the setup is in stereo.

11) Check the fuse if no signal is coming out of a speaker. If it is blown, lower the gain and replace it with a matching fuse.

While replacing small speakers is routine in the studio, changing the main big studio speakers is not. This is usually taken care of by the technical staff. When the big speakers do need changing, help the technical staff with the change just for the experience.

ADDITIONAL SPEAKERS

Some sessions require a single speaker between the main stereo pair to monitor in mono. Other sessions, such as movie soundtracks, use five or more speakers surrounding the engineer. No matter what unusual speaker configuration is used, you should know how and why it's hooked up that way.

Some mix machines have a tiny speaker on the meter bridge that is used to monitor signal on tape or input to the machine. Some engineers check the sound of their mixes through these tiny mono speakers. This gives an indication of how the mix will come across on a tiny radio or television speaker. If it comes across well on the radio, it's a hit. To heck with melody, musicianship and talent, it's gotta sound good.

SPEAKERS FOR CUE

In the studio, some singers prefer to use speakers instead of headphones for their cue mix. This is so the singer can hear himself without the bulk and constraint of headphones. When the equipment in Figure 5.3 is set up correctly, very little leakage from the speakers will be recorded.

107

To set this up, place two small matching speakers at ear level in front of the singer, forming a triangle between the speakers and the microphone. Connect one speaker out-of-phase with the other, then send a mono signal through the cue send. These mono signals from each speaker cancel each other when they reach the microphone. If the singer is standing in the proper spot in the studio, the song is heard, but not recorded. The sound for the singer is a bit odd, as everything is out of phase.

In the control room, some musicians prefer a pair of speakers directly in front of them as they record. This may give the added impact needed to get the creative juices flowing. The musician may be off axis to the main monitors, but having speakers directly in front of him lets him hear everything clear and up front.

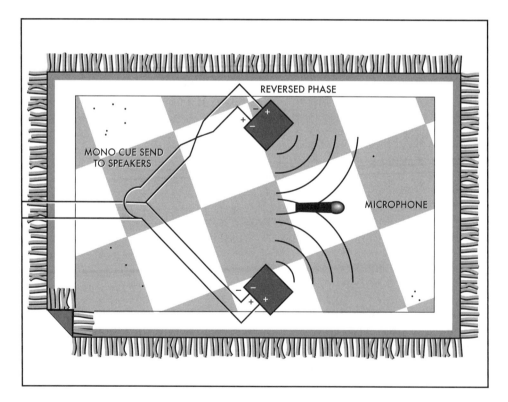

Figure 5.3 Studio Speaker Cue Setup

ANALYZATION AND EQUALIZATION

Professional control rooms are occasionally analyzed with a spectrum analyzer to check the frequency response. White noise, a wide band noise with equal energy per octave, is sent through the large studio monitors while the spectrum analyzer displays the control room's frequency highs and lows. Any errant frequencies are then added or removed with external equalization to dial in the flattest frequency response. The equalizer used is usually housed near the main amplifiers, and is set by either the chief engineer or head of technical. While a spectrum analyzer gives a general view of how the control room sounds, most engineers will set the monitor equalization with their ears, using the analyzer only as a reference.

Many small speakers have an equalizer control in or on them. When the settings must be changed, write the setting down on a piece of paper. Again, don't make a pencil mark on someone's equipment or instrument.

. . . .

Summary

Chapter Five explained how to handle outboard equipment and speakers for a session:

- Placement and connection of standard outboard equipment racks.

- Setup and use of click generators.

- Placement and connection of speakers in the control room and studio.

- Control room analyzation and equalization.

CHAPTER SIX

. . . .

Console and Patchbay

As you may have realized, this book is not an equipment manual, so full details of equipment operations and audio terms are not included. While it does not explain how everything works, it does try to emphasize the importance of understanding all the equipment in the studio, especially the console and patchbay.

The console, also called the board, is the heart of the studio. It combines all input signals, processes them, and sends these combined signals to a recording machine and/or monitor system. There are many different makes and models of consoles, from large and complex to quite simple. Some recording engineers are large and quite simple, but that is for another book.

Most consoles are broken down into three sections: The input section is where the signal reaches the console and is processed. The monitor section is either the live inputs from the studio, or the returns from the multitrack. The center section, although not always in the center, houses the master sends and returns, the main studio gain, the talkback section, the oscillator, and access to monitoring other external sources in the control room, such as CD and DAT machines.

The patchbay centralizes all channel access points on the console, plus all inputs and outputs of the outboard equipment in the control room. This lets the user bypass defective or unwanted components, add additional signal processing and re-route signal flow. As well, all inputs and outputs of all the recording machines and microphone panel inputs and outputs are accessed at the patchbay.

NORMALS

A *normal* is a signal's hard wired route. Common normals in a studio are sends and returns. Figure 6.1 shows that send 1 is normalled to echo chamber 1, then returns to stereo return 1. If you turn up send 1 on any channel, that signal will automatically route to echo chamber 1, then come back to the normalled returns without having to be patched. Unless the patch is broken, a signal will route to and from its destination.

See the flow of a signal's standard hard wired route, and the patchbay access points for the input and output of the send, and the input and output of the return. In this instance, the send is mono and the return is stereo.

Also normalled are the inputs and outputs of the console. Depending on the mode, or status of the console, the channel inputs are normalled from either the microphone inputs, or the track returns of the multitrack. (See later in this chapter for the console's different operating statuses.)

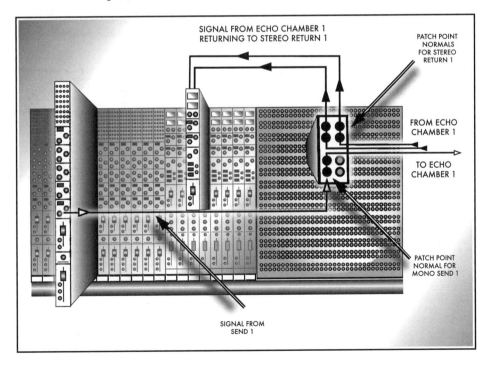

SIGNAL FROM ECHO CHAMBER 1
RETURNING TO STEREO RETURN 1

PATCH POINT
NORMALS
FOR STEREO
RETURN 1

FROM ECHO
CHAMBER 1

TO ECHO
CHAMBER 1

PATCH POINT
NORMAL FOR
MONO SEND 1

SIGNAL FROM
SEND 1

Figure 6.1 *Normals in the Patchbay*

BREAKING THE NORMALS

All normals have access points at the patchbay for re-routing. But just because a normal signal is re-routed does not automatically mean it stops going to its original destination. Half normal patch points allow re-routing of the signal without interrupting the existing signal flow. Figure 6.2 shows that when patching from the half normal output of multitrack return 4 into channel line input 5, signal continues to return to channel line input 4, as well as to channel line input 5. The return from track 5 has become inactive because channel line input patch points are full normal— totally interrupting the signal flow.

To stop multitrack return 4 from returning to channel line input 4, you could deadpatch channel line input 4. A deadpatch is a patchcord connected to the input of a full normal patch point meant to interrupt the standard normal signal path.

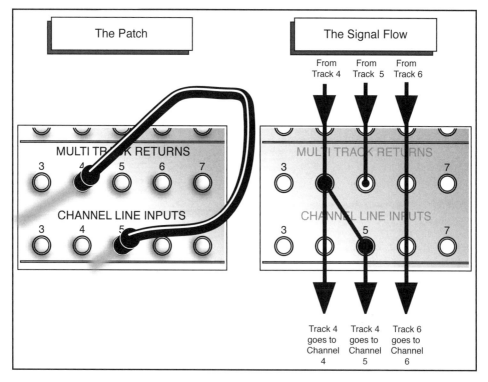

Figure 6.2 *Normal and Half Normal Patch Points*

In this instance, the microphone outputs are full normal. If you insert a patchcord into the output of microphone patch point 8, the signal flow is interrupted. The microphone signal does not proceed on its standard path on to channel 8. In most patchbays, the top row of patches are the microphone outputs from the microphone input panels in the studio room, and the row underneath are the microphone inputs to each channel. This row is used when, for example, a microphone in the studio room is plugged into microphone input number 8, and the engineer wants the microphone in channel 9 on the console.

THE CONSOLE

While many engineers want to set the equalization and outboard settings themselves, most expect the assistant engineer to complete the bussing and patching before they arrive for the session. The engineer should be able to come in, sit at the console and be assured that everything is complete and correct according to his specifications on the input/setup sheet, Figure 2.3.

ZEROING THE CONSOLE

Before starting a session, the console needs to be zeroed and cleaned. Zeroing the console means returning all the knobs, faders, and subgroups to their standard off position. This should have been done by the assistant from the previous session, as you will do at the end of your session. Dust off the surface of the console, and erase any pencil marks or grease marks.

LABELLING THE SCRIBBLE STRIP

After zeroing the console, label the scribble strip, Figure 6.3. The scribble strip, commonly known as the strip, is the area of the console above the faders, where the individual channel information is written. Run a length of white adhesive tape across the console strip. It's not convenient to totally re-write the scribble strip every time the song is changed, so this strip is removed and kept for future sessions within a project.

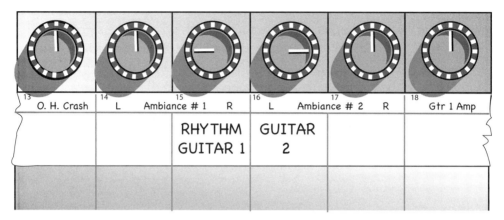

Figure 6.3 *The Scribble Strip Label*

Each song has its own scribble strip, which is updated as more instruments are recorded. This strip is used until the song is mixed, when another strip is made to suit the engineer's choice of track layouts.

To retain the stickiness of the adhesive tape, store the scribble strips on the glass partitions between the studio and control room—of course without blocking out the engineer's view of the studio. When the project is over, roll up the strips of tape and store them with the rest of the paperwork.

When adhesive tape is not used for the scribble strip, try china markers or erasable felt pens to write directly on the console strip. However you choose to label the console, here are a few guidelines to follow—

• Write on the strip the way the engineer does. He may prefer different instruments or functions written in different colors, or double-thick strips of tape, or perhaps a line drawn between each input.

• Sometimes running adhesive tape across the strip hides the channel numbers on the console. Write the channel number on the corner of each input, or place the tape low enough on the strip so as not to cover the channel numbers.

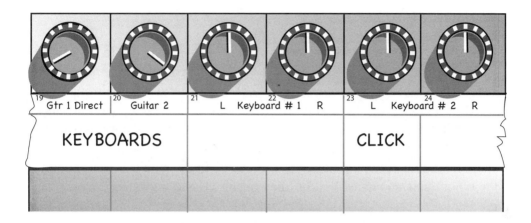

19 Gtr 1 Direct	20 Guitar 2	21 L Keyboard # 1 R	22	23 L Keyboard # 2 R	24
KEYBOARDS				CLICK	

- Sometimes the strip must contain both the inputs to, and the returns from, the multitrack, so you may need to write a lot of information on the small space allotted. When the channel is being used as a microphone input, mark down the instrument, the microphone and, if used, the microphone pad.

- Write the part, for example "chorus guitar," and sometimes the musician. Four channels of accordion might need the name of each musician on the strip. One drummer wouldn't.

- For an effects return, label the send, the effect, and perhaps the length or depth of the unit. For example "Send 1—Echo Plate 1—2.5 seconds."

DIGITAL SCRIBBLE STRIP

In digital, there is no such thing as a scribble strip. Individual tracks and returns are labelled beneath each channel's respective return. Digital consoles include a small area for labelling. As in the traditional scribble strip, this is where you mark any information that the engineer will need, such as send and return information.

Again, label the tracks before the recording begins so the regions can be correctly identified in the regions list.

CONSOLE STATUS MODE

Before continuing with the setup of the console, switch it to the correct operating status. The modern console works in two statuses. *Microphone* status and *line* status. In *microphone,* or *record* status the main inputs to the channel faders are normalled from the input panels, with the multitrack returns in the monitor faders. In *line,* or *mix* status, the channel faders are returns from the multitrack, with microphones in the monitor faders. For example, a microphone plugged into input 12 in the studio is normalled to the main fader on channel 12 on the console. Basic tracks are recorded in this status.

In line status, the main faders are not microphone inputs, but line inputs, such as returns from the multitrack, or returns from outboard equipment. For example, track 12 on the multitrack is normalled to track 12 on the console. Sometimes these returns are not normalled to the console, and must be patched. Overdubs and mixing tend to be done in this status.

As the status of the whole console can be changed from one status to the other, so can the individual channels. For example, with the console in *microphone* status, the click generator might be introduced into the channel at line level. This channel is changed from *microphone* to *line* status using the *flip* button.

Some modern consoles operate in tandem with the recording machines. The individual tracks are accessed from controls on the console. For example, if track 18 is to be recorded, a button on channel 18 on the console is pressed to activate *record-ready* on the multitrack. With the console in the correct status, begin the bussing using the input/setup sheet.

BUSSING

The busses, sometimes called group outputs, are the numbered buttons on each channel of the console. Busses are sends that normally route signal from the individual channels on the console to the tracks on the multitrack.

For example, if buss 3 on channel 14 is pressed, signal from channel 14 is sent to, and recorded on track 3, unless the signal path is broken at the patchbay. Some smaller 8-buss consoles use cross-normalling, which routes signal from buss 1 to tracks 1, 9, and 17 without using patchcords. The buss outputs are accessed at the patchbay, so they can also be used to send signal to outboard effects.

According to the input/setup sheet, most of the instruments are bussed to single tracks. However, notice that the overhead microphones in inputs 11, 12 and 13 are bussed to tracks 9 and 10. This means the engineer wants a stereo spread of the crash cymbal overhead microphones (inputs 12 and 13) and he wants to combine the ride cymbal overhead microphone (input 11) on channels 9 and 10 as well. The ride cymbal channel is bussed to tracks 9 and 10 so the engineer can pan more signal to one track, and less to the other track.

Each buss has a master trim (an overall gain control used to lower the output level of each buss) sometimes called an attenuator, on its own channel. For example, the master trim for buss 25 appears on channel 25 on the console. Because it is a trim, the master buss level starts at 0dB, then attenuates.

When two busses on a channel are pressed, the buss output level is the same on both. For example, if buss 25 is patched into a delay, and buss 26 is patched into an echo plate, pressing busses 25 and 26 on any channel would send the same signal level to both the delay and the echo plate. If you wanted the output of buss 25 lowered, you could use the master trim on channel 25, and this lowers all signals bussed to 25.

Though the input/setup sheet states that some busses will need outboard patched into the signal, buss all channels to the multitrack first, then complete the patching.

THE PATCHBAY

Each patchbay is wired to suit each individual control room, so once you understand the patchbay and how the normals are routed, you will have a good idea how all the equipment in the room integrates.

Although you will spend much of your time before, during, and after the session setting up equipment, an important part of your job is setting up, keeping track of, and breaking down the patchbay. (See Chapter Eight for more on patching.) Watching the patchbay can be very exciting. For now, guidelines include—

• Understand absolutely everything about the patchbay. Every patch point in the bay is there for a reason. Visualizing the signal flow helps in understanding how the engineer wants things patched. Think like an engineer.

• Patch in the direction of signal flow. For example, to insert a limiter into a channel, patch out of the insert send on a channel, into the limiter, out of the limiter, back into the insert return. Insert returns are access patch points, either *pre* or *post* equalization, on each channel to allow additional processing, for example inserting a limiter to be patched into the signal.

• Microphone patch points and line patch points are not compatible.

• One output patch can *mult*, or split the signal into two other inputs, but two outputs cannot mult into one input.

• Leave a note pad by the patchbay to organize everything from writing down patches to taking lunch orders.

• If possible, use similarly colored patchcords for similar functions, for example red cords for sends, green for returns. Use cables of the same lengths for stereo returns, not one long cable and one short cable.

- Use appropriate patchcords with good connectors at both ends. Sometimes patchcords lose their end casings, leaving the connecting wires exposed. Remove these patchcords and get them repaired, as using them may yield unpredictable results. They also cut your finger when you push them into the patchbay.

- While making the patch, mute the returning channels on the console to avoid a loud pop in the speakers, unless this will deaden an active microphone.

- When patching in stereo, double check that the left stays left, and the right stays right.

- Some outboard equipment has an in/out switch on the faceplate, or front panel that allows it to be deactivated while still in line. If there is an in/out switch, take the signal out and let the engineer activate it at his leisure.

- When testing equipment for input and output levels, patch out of the oscillator into the unit to see input on the meters. As the return of the unit is not yet patched, you will see the input to the unit, but not the return levels at the console.

- There are various ways to tell if the return from the unit is working properly. Some consoles have access to line input levels to meters. If this is the case, patch the return into the meters on the console, and watch it react with the instrument being sent to it.

Some consoles don't have access to line input meters, so again, the best way is to patch the return into a nearby recording machine, such as a stand-alone CD burner in *input*, and monitor through headphones. When you have your proper parameters and levels to and from the unit, continue with the rest of the patches.

MICROPHONE INPUTS

Once all equipment is set up, test each signal to and from the console for correct flow. With all the different cables, patches and busses, some signals may be inadvertently misrouted. Turning up the gain on one channel may tell you a microphone is working, but not which one.

Bring in a runner to help test the microphones. Have him scratch, or tap the head of the microphone as you listen. When the signal flow of each channel is tested, the inputs to the machine are not normally monitored. The multitrack returns are monitored so if there is any problem with the complete signal path from microphone to console to multitrack, and back to the monitor section of the console, it will be immediately noticed. Now begin testing the inputs.

1) With the console in *microphone* status, and multitrack machine in *sync* status, lower the control room monitor gain. Condenser microphones need a +48 volt power source, called phantom power, supplied at the console. Turn on the phantom power on any condenser microphone channels, and set the control room monitor gain at a moderate level.

2) Switch all the applicable tracks to *record-ready*, and set the multitrack to *auto-input*.

3) To check that you are monitoring the right source, bring up a few faders and listen for any room noise. If you hear no activity in the studio, trace down the reason. The console or multitrack machine may be in the wrong operating status, the amplifiers may be off, or you may have lost your hearing.

4) Start with input 1, the microphone on the bass amplifier. According to the input/setup sheet, a Neumann U-47 with a cardioid polar pattern is in front of the bass amplifier, plugged into input 1, and bussed to track 2 on the multitrack.

5) Double check with the runner that any pads or roll-offs have been set on the microphones, according to the input/setup sheet.

6) As the runner taps the first microphone, bring up main fader on channel 1. As channel 1 is bussed to track 2 on the multitrack machine, look at the input meter 2 on the machine to see any input.

7) Bring up monitor fader 2 to hear the signal returning to the console.

8) If any outboard is patched into the signal, check that it is working correctly, with no buzzes or hums. When you have confirmed the signal is working and routed correctly, move on to the next channel on the console.

LINE INPUTS

Not all inputs to the console are microphone inputs. The second input to the console is a direct, or line input from the direct box on the bass guitar. If the bass is connected, the runner might tap a string, or if it is a keyboard, he might press a key for you to hear if it is working.

If the input is just a loose ¼" cable waiting for an instrument to be plugged in, the runner can hold the cable and tap the end of the jack, creating crackles and clicks on the input channel. This will be enough to tell if the signal is getting into the console. Once the line inputs have been checked, turn off the channels before the musician arrives and plugs in. Continue with the rest of the inputs until all are working properly or a problem is discovered.

CHASING, TRACING AND REPLACING

Sometimes, for any number of reasons, you cannot hear the signal so the problem needs to be traced. Have the runner speak into the microphone, or tap the line input, while you watch at the input meter on the multitrack. If you turn the monitor gain way up to check if the signal is coming through, remember to lower it again. If you leave the monitor gain turned up, when the problem is discovered, the channel will return much too loud.

To trace a signal that is not working:

- Determine where the problem originates. If you see signal reaching the multitrack machine input meters, you know the problem is not with the microphone or the input section of the channel, the problem is in the monitor section.

- Follow the signal path. If you see no signal getting to the multitrack, the problem is in the studio or at the input stage. Trace the problem by the process of elimination. Listen to the input of the channel where it enters the console. If signal can't be heard, then the problem probably lies within the studio.

- Turn the channel off and have the runner trace the cables in the studio. The cable or microphone may need replacing.

- Check the console and the patchbay. Is the phantom power on? Is the signal bussed and patched correctly? Is the channel in the right status? Is everything turned on? Is anything blocking the signal at the patchbay? Eventually, you will find and fix the problem.

CUE SENDS

As mentioned in the section on headphones, different sections of the band will want their own cue mix. Musicians want the same feel with headphones that they get during rehearsals. A drummer may want lots of bass, and very little guitars, while the guitarist may want lots of drums and no keyboards. To do this, the engineer may set up any number of independent cue sends. Console limitations may dictate that some cue mixes be in mono, not stereo.

The cue mix also may be the actual monitor mix off the console. When the engineer changes any levels or panning on his monitor mix, these changes will also occur in the headphones. The input/setup sheet shows the drummer receives cue send 1, and the rest receive cue send 2. While the runner is speaking into a microphone in the studio, turn up the applicable cue sends. When the runner hears himself in the headphones, the cue is working properly.

MASTER SENDS AND RETURNS

Most consoles have between four to eight sends on each channel. The center section houses the master cue send, and is used to change the overall send levels and sometimes equalization, depending on the individual console. There is also a corresponding number of stereo returns in the center section used to return effects without tying up individual channels.

Don't raise the master cue send levels all the way. If the cues don't appear loud enough, raise them on the individual cue boxes. During the session, if the musician wants more overall cue level, and the master send is all the way up, the individual level on each channel would have to be raised, changing the cue mix. It is more convenient for the engineer to simply turn up the overall mix, than each individual channel. Once the cue mix is set and correct, it shouldn't need changing.

TALKBACK

The talkback section of the console has a built-in microphone that lets the people in the control room talk with the people in the studio. It is also used to slate each take. The engineer slates the take by speaking into the talkback microphone, and recording the song title and take number before the song starts.

Many studios have some sort of remote button on the end of a long cable that, when pressed, activates the talkback microphone on the console. The producer can just lean back in the control room, press the remote control button, and talk to the studio. Sometimes he thinks that the remote he is holding is the actual microphone, much like a CB radio, and talks directly to it not realizing it's only the button that activates the microphone on the console. This creates peals of laughter within the assistant engineer community, especially when no one tells him.

As with the master send levels, check the talkback level for proper output before the session begins. Better the level is too quiet than too loud.

Here are a few guidelines for dealing with the talkback in session—

- Be quiet when the talkback button is pressed. Rustling papers and casual conversation in the background comes through loud and clear.

- Talk through the talkback only if you are engineering, or if you are talking to the engineer in the studio. It is not your place to make comments to the band through the talkback.

- Place the engineer's headphones away from the talkback as they may feed back when the talkback button is pushed.

- Leave the control room monitor button muted. When the engineer wants to talk to a musician one-to-one, he may press the control room monitor *cut* button, walk into the studio, and speak to a musician. He obviously doesn't want the people in the control room to hear him.

. . . .

Summary

Chapter Six explained setting up the console and patchbay for the session:

- Understanding the normals within the studio and control room.

- Preparing the console for the session, including zeroing the channels, writing out the scribble strip, switching the console to the correct operating status, setting all the busses and completing all the pre-session patching.

- Creating a digital session setup including all inputs, outputs, subgroups, plug-ins and templates.

- Going through each channel with a runner and testing all signal flow from the studio to the multitrack, then back to the console.

- Setting the cue and master send levels.

124

CHAPTER SEVEN

· ·

Session Priorities

Once all the equipment is set up and the session is ready to go, here are a few guidelines to help you keep the session running smoothly and efficiently for everyone:

- Keep up with the engineer. Understand the complete signal flow of the session, including all patching, bussing, and signal routing. You can't tell if something isn't reacting correctly if you don't know or understand the signal path. If he tells you to do something that seems wrong, you can question it because you are right there with him. Zero in on his wavelength. The ideal situation is to know what he wants before he tells you.

- Keep the session rolling. All changes must be fast and efficient. There is no time to chat while changing the song or setting up equipment. If someone asks you to do something, wait until the equipment is set up and the engineer has everything he needs to continue.

- If you don't know something, say you don't know. If you did something wrong, admit you did something wrong. You and the engineer must be on the same team. This isn't like the medical profession, where you can fake it as you go.

- Ensure that all tracksheets, recording maps, takesheets, labels and notes are always up to date, clear and complete.

- Set priorities for each situation. If the engineer wants a limiter in the vocal channel, a sandwich from the deli, a fire extinguisher, and details of studio scheduling, you need to prioritize. You wouldn't leave the room to order a sandwich before making the patches, and it seems more important to put out the fire before asking the manager about studio availability.

- Continually scan the room to confirm everything is acting and reacting as it should, including the inputs to the machines, the meters on all the equipment, the console, the outboard, and even the musicians. Keep all doors closed, and listen for any fans or air conditioners that may be on. If you see or hear something wrong, tell the engineer before he presses the *record* button.

- Don't let the engineer record over anything. When he puts a track in *record-ready*, check the tracksheet and confirm the proper signal is going to the proper track. This should become second nature. When he changes something on the console, lean over his shoulder and check that his change is correct. If he changes the signal path incorrectly, or busses something incorrectly, go over and quietly point it out. It's like looking after your grandfather—he can teach you a lot, but you always need to keep an eye on him.

- When there is a problem, don't let the session know. The clients should never know of any troubles or malfunctions. If a problem occurs, such as equipment not working, simply work around it without making a big deal of it. Either quietly tell the engineer or slip him a note. Of course, urgent problems call for urgent actions. If he is about to record over an important track, don't slip him a note telling him so.

- If the engineer makes a mistake, don't let the rest of the session know. The musicians and the producer must have faith in him, and you shouldn't undermine that. Don't make him look like an idiot in front of everyone. He can do that himself.

- Don't wait for the engineer to ask you to do things—just do them. If someone in the session asks the engineer to play a specific section of a song, find it before the engineer asks you. If you hear the engineer tell a musician he is going to put an equalizer on his instrument, don't wait for him to tell you, just make the patch. If he tells a musician to wait because a microphone needs changing, be out the door to change it. As well, if you know how the engineer likes certain equipment set up, do it without being asked. For example, if a vocal overdub is next, and you know the engineer always uses a specific equalizer and limiter in a certain order, set it up without him having to ask you.

- Watch the musicians to make sure they have everything they need to be comfortable and ready for the session. When something needs changing, such as headphones or cables, change them fast. Occasionally listen to the headphone cue mixes to hear if anything is unusually loud or quiet. If you hear something wrong, tell the engineer. Some musicians won't hear anything specific, they will just know something isn't right in their headphone mix.

- All equipment must be turned on and ready for use. When something is not working correctly, label it 'out of order' and get the technical staff on it. Check all machines for proper input levels.

- Do something good early in the project. This should earn you a goodly amount of trust throughout the rest of the project from the producer and engineer, enough perhaps for them to consider you for some minor engineering. This will also allow you some freedom with small mistakes. If they feel you are doing a great job, small mistakes will be forgotten. If they feel you are doing a poor job, that same small mistake becomes a large mistake.

- If you are working with an engineer you have never worked with before, wait a few days then ask him how you are doing, and what you can do to help him more effectively. This will show him that you really care about doing the best job you possibly can.

127

- Stay in the control room. The engineer needs you to set up equipment, change routing, fetch coffee, answer questions or address any problems. He doesn't want to have to hunt around for you when he needs a patch. You can't keep up if you are in the lobby playing video games.

- A musician may become distracted with you moving around in the control room, or worse, staring at her while she sings. These are times when you dim the lights, settle into the darkness and quietly do your job.

- Don't change the settings on anything without the engineer knowing about it. If something doesn't seem right, mention it, and let him deal with it. During recording, he has many things to listen to, so any setting changes may not be immediately noticed. If you must make a change, for instance when the engineer is out of the room, mention it when he returns. Keep him up to date.

- Don't start talking about other sessions. Something that happened last week in another session may seem funny to you, but the client doesn't want to hear it. He wants to concentrate on his project, not be interrupted with your so-called 'humorous' little anecdotes.

- Be quiet. Your job is to assist the engineer, not to give your opinion. There is nothing much worse than an assistant who won't shut up. Of course, as you get more comfortable with a musician, producer and engineer you can decide how casual you can be. Take a second to think before asking any stupid questions.

- Maintain quiet in the control room. What the session is working on is all that should be heard. Use headphones to find samples, set delay times, or find sections of music. Switch the channel off when changing cables, patches, microphones or their settings, or anything involved with signal. Lower the monitor level when the analog machine is in rewind so the tape whizzing past the heads can't be heard. A quiet control room also means not yelling across the room to the engineer. Go over and speak to him, not to everyone in the control room.

- Get the client in and out on time. Warn the engineer if another session is scheduled to start right after yours. But don't tell the musician, leave that to the engineer or producer. It can be a difficult situation when the next client is waiting to start, and the engineer wants a little more time to finish the mix. Of course, if you are working into the night, or if the sessions are locked out, being out on time may not be an issue. A lockout is when the client rents the studio full-time, 24 hours a day.

- Stay awake. Don't even yawn (it's contagious.) The client should feel that you are in complete control, not about to doze off. This may sound funny, but when working long hours, falling asleep can easily happen. Having finished all your work, you must sit around the control room and watch everyone else work. These are the times when you gently slip into the arms of Morpheus.

- Don't sit around and read when there is work to do. It's fine if you are reading a manual, or researching something for the engineer, but in general, don't do it unless you have done absolutely everything that needs doing. The client may not have total faith in you if he sees you with your feet up on the console reading an Archie comic.

- Don't treat any project casually. No one knows who the next major stars and producers will be, or where the next hit record will come from. You always want to do your best for the people you are working with.

- Don't go into the studio when something is being recorded. That magical take can happen at any time, and it will be unusable if you can be heard clomping around in the background. If you absolutely must go into the studio while recording, be as quiet as possible.

- Sit at the console next to the engineer whenever you can. This will give you the engineer's sonic perspective, so when he makes a change you can hear what he is hearing. If he asks you to move, then move, but return when you can. Of course, if there is only one extra chair, the producer has rank.

- Avoid drugs and alcohol. To get ahead in the studio, you must be on the ball. It is important for everyone in the session to have full confidence in your abilities and the decisions you are expected to make. If you make a mistake under the influence, it will not be forgotten.

- Wear earplugs, even if no one else does. Don't let some deaf recording engineer blast you with loud volumes for hours on end. Use them at any sign of increased volumes, in the studio or out. In the good old days, the gauge of having a good time at a concert was directly related to the amount of ringing in your ears. "I had such a good time at the concert that my ears are still ringing, and the show was last year." Your hearing is your livelihood, protect it.

TELEPHONE PROTOCOL

Your job also involves answering the studio telephone. This may be the outside world calling in, or just elsewhere on the premises. Some studios have phone systems more complicated than a jumbo jet cockpit and invariably more difficult to master. However, every call is important, so learn how to use the studio's phone system.

You should not take any personal calls while in session. If you must take an important call, take it somewhere out of the control room. And letting your own cellphone ring during the session is unacceptable. Leave your phone outside the studio.

There will be times when you must judge whether someone wants to talk privately, like when the producer's girlfriend or wife calls—or when they both call. If you and he are the only ones in the control room, go into the studio so he can talk privately. Keep your eye on the control room to see when he is through, then return to the control room.

If you have a message for someone in another studio, go in and tell the assistant on that session. Do not barge in and tell the whole room.

THE DOOR

Some studios have a little button to open the front door from the control room. Some may even have a video monitor to see who is at the door. In some studios, you are responsible for answering the door. Be careful who you let in, as you don't want to unknowingly open the door to a pack of overzealous fans to run rampant through the studios.

Never let anyone into the session without checking with the producer. People from the outside world like to stop by and hang out during sessions. Sessions are closed unless you are told otherwise. Artists can become uncomfortable when there is a strange face in the control room. And this industry has some strange faces! If you are not working on the session—even if you know everyone there—keep out. No one is allowed into the session except the musicians, the producer, the engineering staff (this means you) and sometimes a runner, who might sit in the corner to quietly watch and learn.

WHEN THE COMPANY REPRESENTATIVES STOP BY

At some point during most larger budget record projects, the financial backers, such as representatives from the record company, may come by to hear how the project is going. This is the time the band is trying to win approval from the 'money people.'

When these people come by, don't make any jokes or comments about anything. Do the job, remain silent, and stay in the control room. Make absolutely sure the place is clean and organized. A messy workplace will create a more anxious atmosphere, giving them the impression that the studio and staff may not be up to scratch. Offer beverages such as coffee, tea or soda, then clean up the empty containers.

Before everyone arrives, ask which song to play first. Cue the song up correctly, and play only what the producer wants them to hear. If necessary use headphones so no one hears anything but the correct song. Play the complete song from the beginning to the end. If you are unsure of which take to play, quietly ask the producer.

COFFEE AND TEA

Most people in the recording industry think the mainstay of being an assistant engineer is getting coffee or tea. Well, it is! Good coffee or tea flows through a studio, so ask the studio manager to spring for the good stuff, and learn how to make it. Please follow directions.

Keep a supply of clean cups, spoons, honey, sugar, and cream. Remember what everyone takes in their coffee or tea, and place the cup where no one will be electrocuted if it gets spilled. Find a small table to put next to the engineer for his cup. Never put a beverage on the console, or any other electronic equipment. During long sessions, take it upon yourself to bring a fresh cup of coffee to a weary engineer.

Use real cups, not Styrofoam. They give you Styrofoam cups down at the "Ten Minit Car Lube." Go the extra mile, above and beyond what is expected. People want to feel that they are important clients. Styrofoam cups are not re-usable and often become ash trays half full of cold coffee. Dealing with real cups means also being a dishwasher. Welcome to the glamorous world of recording!

ORDERING OUT

When people in the session need to order food, you will do all the organizing. Keep a collection of menus from neighborhood delis and restaurants. When everyone decides what they want to order, write the items down clearly, with how much money each person gave you. Place the order from the lobby, not the control room. Hopefully there will be a receptionist or a runner to deal with food orders.

If no one else is available, you may be elected to run out to fetch the order. Always ask for a receipt. Before leaving the studio, clear it with the engineer. He may need you to set something up before you leave. Ask him to watch the telephone and the door while you are gone. However, most independent engineers won't feel obliged to answer your phone.

If the food is being delivered, check that the order is correct and complete before the delivery person leaves. No one wants tongue and liver when they ordered a chef's salad. Check for correct change and remember, if you want good reliable service from most delis, you have to tip.

Don't let the delivery person into the control room. This is a private session where creativity must be allowed to run free. It can't really run free with Bubba, the delivery boy standing there waiting to be paid. Large budget sessions sometimes let dinner orders go on the work order, leaving the record company responsible for payment.

EATING YOUR LUNCH

Your job rarely entails a lunch break. If the band doesn't stop to eat, then neither do you. If you must eat, slip out of the room during a break. If there is work to do, you'll just have to wait to eat your lunch. Do not eat your lunch in front of everyone. Nothing is more distracting than someone eating a Limburger cheese and onion sandwich next to a musician who is trying to concentrate on a part.

I don't want to sound like your mother, but wash your hands after lunch. Handling tapes, tracksheets or equipment with greasy little fingers is not the greatest idea. When everyone stops to eat, they might leave the studio entirely and enjoy their meal in the control room or the lobby. This can be a great time mid-session to do a quick studio cleanup. Of course, this translates into your dinner getting cold, while everyone else enjoys a hot meal. You will also clean up after everyone has finished eating. No one can be expected to be creative amongst leftover fast food wrappers. During jingle sessions, if the client is Burger King, don't eat a Big Mac.

DOWN TIME

Down time occurs when the session is unable to proceed due to malfunctioning equipment. When something directly affecting the session occurs, such checking the alignment, changing speakers, or a power outage, the clock is stopped and the technical staff is called in to solve the problem.

If power does go down, first mute the monitors. If the power goes out unexpectedly, it can come back on just as unexpectedly. The amplifiers and machines powering up again with the monitors on would create quite a loud speaker-blowing pop. Second, unwind both sides of the tape on any open reel machine to move it out of the sensor paths and away from the heads, then switch the multitrack machine off. If tape is left on the heads when the power is restored, the power spike may stretch the tape or create a click on the tape where it touches the heads. Many electronic devices tend to lose their set programs when powered down unless the settings have been stored in the internal memory. When minor breakdowns occur, the offending equipment is either removed or bypassed at the patchbay with a minimum of fanfare.

Don't let the client know about any minor technical difficulties if the difficulties don't affect the outcome of the session. Of course, if the control room is flooded with two feet of water, the client may clue in. When legitimate down time occurs, state the time aloud, and that the session is now on down time. Keep exact records of when the down time began, and when the session started working again. The client will invariably question the length of down time written on the work order.

Clients may see how down time works and try to shave some time off their bill. They may say that setting up the equipment should be classed as down time, so the total hours billed should be lowered. They might spend too much time working out a musical part, or waste time talking on the phone during session, then try to pressure the assistant to pass this off as down time on the work order. As some studios pay the assistants for the time billed to the client, this may mean that you don't get paid for down time. Why should you not make any money while the musicians, producer, and engineer are probably rich enough combined to buy the Taj Mahal?

WHEN THINGS GO WRONG

When I was starting out as an assistant engineer, I accidentally spilled a full can of soda into the main faders on the new console. I panicked and ran around trying to figure out how to switch the console off before it exploded. Later the engineer chastised me, not for spilling the soda into the console, but for showing my lack of ability to handle a crisis in front of the client. Of course, the session was halted while the cleanup took place.

The studio manager later asked me what I was going to do about this situation. I said I'd probably just buy another soda. The lesson here is, before going into the studio, know what the procedures are in case of emergencies. Hopefully you will never need to use them, but check the exact location of the first aid kit, the fire extinguishers, and all fire exits.

GETTING TECHNICAL

TECHNICAL STAFF

Most big and medium size recording studios have qualified technical staff to do all the equipment repairs, upgrades and alignments. They are the behind the scenes workers of the studio that keep the seeming endless array of new, used, ancient, and obsolete equipment operating.

Depending on the size of the studio, the technical department might range from someone coming in occasionally to do repairs and check alignments, to a full crew 24 hours a day. Without a qualified technical staff, the recording studio would soon grind to a rusty halt.

If you really want to understand the workings of equipment in the studio, hang out when the technical staff is doing repairs. Usually, they are happy to explain things if you offer to lend a hand hauling equipment for them. But don't do their job unless you are expected to. The technical staff does not want you stepping on their toes by doing things like changing modules, or reseating cards. When dealing with the technical staff, remember one very important point. Many of them are "$^1/_2$ dB off bias" if you know what I mean. If they like you, they can help you. If they don't like you, they can seriously hurt you. Go out of your way to stay on their good side.

In smaller studios, the assistants often help with the minor repairs. This may involve soldering wires for cables and headphones, tracing any malfunctions, hauling and connecting equipment, and sometimes even doing a bit of carpentry. Helping the technical staff offers you the chance to delve deep into the workings of the studio. For major repairs or upgrades, equipment is either sent out, or a qualified technical person is brought in.

Understanding the electronics and signal flow of the studio gives you a major advantage over someone who doesn't have any electronics experience. However, the technical side of the studio is a bottomless pit. If you are the only employee with a grasp of repairing and upgrading electronic equipment, guess who will be doing all the studio repairs?

THE SHOP

The tech shop, is where most of the equipment is tested and repaired. The shop has all the equipment necessary to keep a studio operational—repair tools, equipment manuals, test equipment, and a nudie calendar. The shop is a good place to hang out and learn, but there are a few important guidelines:

• If you don't have direct permission to take things from the shop, don't. The shop is not normally your work area, it is someone else's.

- When you take or use anything from the shop, put it back where you found it, or your access to the shop may be restricted.

- Reading the equipment manuals to understand how everything works is great, but the best way to learn the operations of equipment in the control room is still the old-fashioned way. Get in there and experiment.

- There may be things taken apart in there, so don't go poking around where you don't belong—such as feeling the smooth and flexible diaphragm of a disassembled microphone. As well, don't take a microphone apart. Repairing headphones or cables is one thing, but the insides of a microphone are delicate, and should only be disassembled by qualified personnel.

- Don't try to fix studio equipment unless you are authorized and totally confident that you can correctly complete the repairs. Most electronic equipment is easy to take apart but not so easy to re-assemble.

MAINTENANCE FORMS

When equipment in the studio is not working properly, use a maintenance form, or trouble sheet, to describe the malfunction. Figure 7.1 shows a problem that isn't drastic enough to stop the session, but enough to warrant the technical staff's attention after the session ends.

Be explicit, stating the exact problem—how the signal was patched, the studio, the date, the engineer, the assistant, the time the problem was discovered and any temporary action taken. For example, the engineer notices a hum on the left return of an echo chamber. Rather than stop the session to trace down the problem, he has you change the patch to another echo chamber, and continues on with the session. The maintenance form is filled out explaining the situation, and the temporary action taken. It is then handed in with the work order after the session. The issue will, you hope, be taken care of before your next session.

MAINTENANCE REPORT NO. 130785

SESSION _____TUFF BEANS_____   DATE _____July 29, Year_____

ENGINEER _____Casey Jones_____   TIME _____6 pm_____

ASSISTANT _____A. Reader_____   STUDIO A ☒ B ☐ C ☐

SYMPTOMS PLEASE BE EXPLICIT - INCLUDE ENVIRONMENT OF PROBLEM

Heard a loud hum in left side of echo chamber # 1.

TEMPORARY ACTION TAKEN:

Used echo chamber # 2

REPAIRED BY: _____   DATE _____

DIAGNOSIS:

PARTS SENT OR ORDERED: _____   DATE: _____

PARTS RECEIVED: _____   DATE: _____

Figure 7.1 *Maintenance Form*

Maintenance forms are numbered so all repairs can be correctly logged, with an explanation of who did the repairs, and what exactly was done. If the problem remains, go back to the original form and confirm the repairs. Sometimes just asking someone from the technical staff to have a quick look at malfunctioning equipment may resolve the problem. If things cannot be immediately repaired, the unit may have to be removed.

DAILY LOG

Write all pertinent information in a daily log. Figure 7.2 shows a running schedule of what happened at what time throughout the session. The log can be a loose leaf book with removable pages, or just a pad of paper. Whatever system you use to log your daily information, keep it organized. A three-ring binder works best, as the pages are removable. The main purpose of a daily log is to keep all information about sessions and equipment together and organized. Sometimes, when a track is recorded during basics, repaired weeks later, then bounced (recorded from one track to another) to another track, tracing down needed information may prove quite a challenge. Any questions about any track must be traceable through the paper trail, or if a computer is the preferred format, the mouse trail.

Copies of setup sheets, lyrics, work orders (optional), maintenance forms, serial numbers for rental equipment, reminders to yourself, and the general day-to-day happenings should all be stored here and organized by time and date.

Also in the log is an up-to-date list with the contents of all storage media, including master tapes, outtake reels, hard drives, rough mix discs, computers and important DVDs, Blu-Ray discs, CDs, or DATs. If anyone wants to find any information about anything on tape, disc or hard drive, all information is right in your log. Anyone in the session can look through the log and easily find all the information.

I was the assistant engineer on a project that had more than 300 multi-track tapes. The daily log was more like a complete set of Funk and Wagnalls encyclopedias.

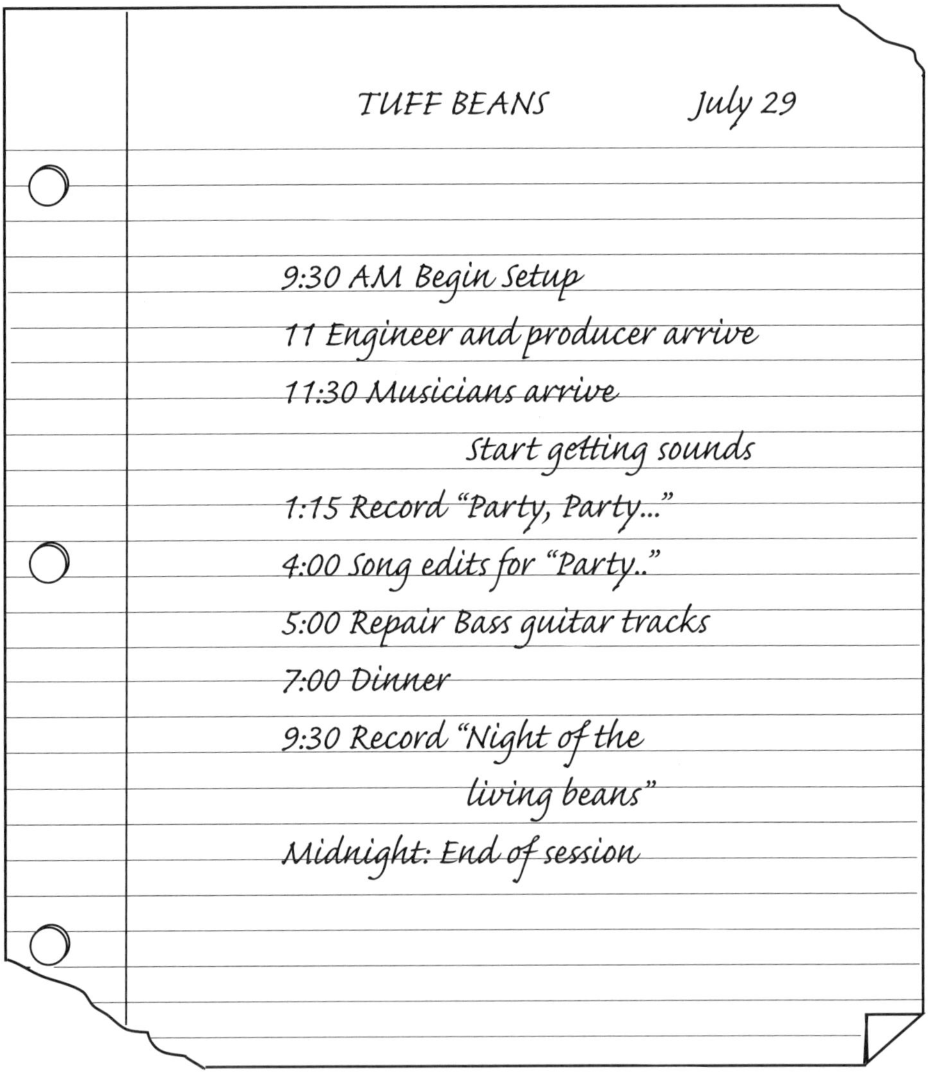

Figure 7.2 *Page from the Daily Log*

INVENTORY SHEETS

Inventory sheets, such as Figure 7.3 are used to track incoming items in the studio. Recording media such as multitrack tape, CDs, DVDs, Blu-Ray discs and DATs used in the session that are charged to the client can all be organized with a simple coding system.

INVENTORY

AEH

SESSION _____ *TUFF BEANS* _____

ENGINEER _____ *Casey Jones* _____   CLIENT _____ *Crapitol Records* _____

ASSISTANT _____ *A. Reader* _____   STUDIO   A [X]   B [ ]   C [ ]

Date	Multitrack	CD	DVD	BLU-RAY	$^1/2''$ Analog	DAT	Additional
July 29	M8 - M13	CD 10-14	DVD 18				2 Batteries
July 30		CD 15-19	DVD 19-20	BR 22			
July 31		CD 25-28					Hard Drive
Aug 2		CD 29-37	DVD 21-22		Reels 4-9	DAT 3-5	

PLEASE INCLUDE INVENTORY USED ON YOUR DAILY WORK ORDER.

Figure 7.3 Inventory Sheet

For example, two boxes with 12 CDs might be individually labeled CD 1 to CD 12, then CD 13 to CD 24, as shown in Figure 7.3. When any item assigned this number is removed from storage, the number is written on the inventory sheet, and the work order for the individual session. Management then cross-references these to keep track of each client's charges. These items are generally kept in or near the tape vault.

MISTAKES

Guess what? Even the best assistants and engineers make mistakes. It is unrealistic to assume you will never make a mistake on your job. If you never have, you aren't working hard enough. Some mistakes will remain between you and the engineer. Some mistakes everyone in the session knows about, and some mistakes the whole recording industry hears about.

There are a few classic assistant engineer mistake stories, such as the Steely Dan story. They allegedly worked on a tape for over a year, and the assistant who was recording the multitrack safety master totally erased the master tape by mistake. According to legend, after realizing his error, he put on his coat and casually walked off into the night, never to return. No one has seen him since.

Then there's the KISS story of how the new assistant stepped on, and snapped, the neck of Ace's rarest guitar.

And the Bon Jovi "Slippery When Wet" story about the assistant who turned the tape over to record a guitar track backward and erased almost the whole keyboard intro of . . . wait a minute, that was me!

The point is, mistakes happen in all jobs. If you erase or delete something important, it can be a blow to your self confidence, and to the confidence of the client. Take it as a learning experience and move on. Again, whenever you make a mistake, tell the engineer. You and the engineer are on the same team, and in this together.

Remain calm and collected, and don't lose your cool in a crisis situation, as you may do more harm than good. You don't want the client to see your inexperience. Everyone needs to feel that you are really in control and know what you are doing. Minor mistakes are usually forgotten, but major mistakes are remembered, and tend to stay with you. If you accidentally burn down the studio, the engineer may be hesitant to use you on his next project.

. . . .

Summary

Chapter Seven explained priorities before, during and after the session:

- Answering the phone and the door; bringing refreshments into the studio, including coffee, tea, and ordering out.

- Down time procedures and recommendations. Dealing with the technical staff, and accessing the maintenance shop.

- Additional paperwork, including maintenance forms and the daily log.

- Mistakes in the studio.

CHAPTER EIGHT

. . . .

Recording Basic Tracks

The first, or primary tracks recorded are called basic tracks, over which overdubs are recorded. There is really no rule determining how the master basic track is established. Depending on the project, the budget, the studio, the band, and many other factors, a song may be recorded one time, or it may be recorded twenty times. The recording may be a single instrument, a small combo, or a full band. The producer may choose one of the twenty, or the engineer might edit together the best sections of all the versions. Once the basic track is established, overdubs may or may not be recorded. Does this clear things up?

Whether the basic tracks are analog or digital, there are a number of standard procedures during the recording.

MEDIA RETRIEVAL

When retrieving the appropriate recording medium:

• Bring enough tapes, CDs, DVDs, DATs, Blu-Ray discs and any other formats used for your session from the vault to the control room, and place them near their respective machines.

• Don't overload yourself. Use a small cart to transport the heavy stuff. Lugging everything to and from the control room every day may be counterproductive to your project, as well as to your back.

- Set everything on a specific table—a space reserved just for media, and don't stack anything too high. Everything must be labeled neatly, well organized and together. If the client sees a messy table and workspace, he loses confidence in you. So please, no cheeseburgers on the media table.

- Load or open the appropriate song or file as described in Chapter Four.

MAKING CHANGES

The engineer should arrive for the session at least a half hour before the session starts. This allows time to check that everything is set up correctly. In the studio, he will adjust the microphones to exactly where he wants them. In the control room, he will go through each channel and check that all signals are correctly routed.

In the recording studio, change is inevitable. (It's usually behind the cushions in the cracks of the sofa.) Although the information from the input sheet may have been initially correct, the engineer will most likely want to make changes to suit the specific needs of the session. This may involve changing or adding microphones, cables, headphones, and patches until he is satisfied with all the sounds.

Murphy's Law dictates that at least one signal that worked perfectly before the session will mysteriously vanish when the engineer listens. It's usually something simple, such as a wrong button pressed. Don't stand there saying, "Well, it was working before," as if it's the engineer's problem. His problem is your problem. Track down why he isn't hearing what he wants to hear.

While you trace and change signals for the engineer, the rest of the people involved in the session may arrive. As they do, help them with their equipment, their coats, their egos, and their spot in the studio. If the musicians are new to the engineer, write each person's name and instrument on a small piece of paper, and put it on or near the console for the engineer to see. Then he doesn't have to refer to the drummer as "Hey Bignose."

145

CHANGING MICROPHONES

As the engineer works on the sounds to be recorded, he may not like the sound of one microphone, or a certain microphone may be faulty. To change the microphone, follow this routine:

1) Before leaving the room to change the microphone, mute the appropriate input channel on the console.

2) Go to the microphone room and find the replacement microphone, and bring it into the studio.

3) Before unplugging the cable from the offending microphone, confirm with the engineer that the correct channel is off. Use the old "finger slice across the throat" routine to confirm the channel on the console is cut. If he doesn't understand this universal gesture, give him another universal gesture he will understand.

4) Unplug the cable and remove the microphone with the shock mount, and set that microphone down on a soft surface. Rather than unscrew the microphone from the stand, try loosening the stand and unscrew the stand from the microphone. This way the microphone is always firmly in your grip.

5) Match the parameters from the original microphone to the new one.

6) Attach the new microphone to the stand, taking care to leave the placement intact, then connect the cable.

7) Signal the engineer to switch the channel on and confirm that the new replacement microphone is working.

8) Return the original microphone to the storage area or, if it is faulty, fill out a maintenance form and take the microphone to the shop.

CHANGING MICROPHONE PARAMETERS

When only the microphone's parameters need changing, again, have the engineer mute the appropriate channel. If you are introducing a pad to the signal, you may need to either flip a switch on the microphone to activate it, install the pad between the microphone head and casing, or connect the pad where the XLR cable merges with the microphone. Keep the initial microphone placement the same, and gently make the change. Note any changes on the setup sheet.

FINAL MICROPHONE PLACEMENT

Just placing a microphone in front of an instrument or amplifier might not be precise enough for some engineers. An engineer may want you to slowly move the microphone around the instrument or amplifier while the musician plays. The engineer will listen in the control room, and signal to you to stop moving the microphone when he hears the elusive sweet spot—where he feels it sounds best. Stop moving the microphone, and tighten the stand, leaving the placement intact. Even the slightest movement may change the sound. Before doing this procedure, please insert your earplugs.

Once the microphones are correctly placed and checked for signal flow, close the isolation booth, if one is being used. If necessary, throw a blanket or two over the booth for added isolation.

CHANGING CABLES

If the engineer tells you to change a cable because signal is not coming through as it should, look over the signal path in the control room to see if a wrong button is pressed, a fader is down, or a patch is wrong. If all seems well on the console, then go replace the cable. Before doing so, again, remind the engineer to mute the channel. After replacing the faulty cable, tie a knot in one end and lay it aside so that it won't be re-used. If the signal still doesn't come through, the original cable probably wasn't faulty—the problem is elsewhere in the signal chain.

CHANGING HEADPHONES

When anyone says they have a problem with their headphones, go out into the studio and ask the player for the headphones. Follow these steps:

1) Listen to the headphones to hear the problem. Check that they are plugged in correctly, and that the headphone box is functioning properly. Test the headphones by plugging them into a nearby headphone box. If they are faulty, quickly exchange them for a usable set. After connecting the new headphones, listen to them before handing them to a musician. Don't change the cue level on the headphone box.

2) Good cue mixes are essential to a player's performance, so take the time to set up a suitable mix for each player. Perhaps the bass player needs more kick drum than everyone else, or maybe the drummer needs more bass guitar. Many studios use "cue stations"—small 8 or 12 channel consoles for each player to set their own cue mix. Individual tracks may include, for example, kick, snare, drums L and R, bass, guitar 1, guitar 2, and vocals. But musicians aren't engineers, so they may need you to set up a mix on each cue station.

3) Replace the whole setup including headphones, cables, and headphone box if the problem remains after the change. Then match the levels on the replacement box with the one being removed. This is not the time to try to solve the problem. Do whatever it takes to keep the session moving forward.

4) After removing the faulty headphones, wrap a piece of adhesive tape around the side that does not work, and set them aside. Fill out a maintenance form, and take the headphones to the shop when convenient.

CHANGING PATCHES

Patches are changed throughout the session, from before the engineer arrives, to after he leaves. Most of your time is spent near the patchbay. Encourage the engineer to let you do all the patches, so you can keep up with the total signal flow.

The patchbay must be organized and up-to-date so the engineer can glance over and see how everything is routed. Remove any patches no longer in use after verifying that they are not needed. After you make a patch, double and triple check that the patch is correct. Any outboard equipment being patched must be switched on and set at a reasonable operating level. The engineer should never have to say "Hey, this is wrong." For example, the engineer asks you to patch in a digital reverb using send 3. You might—

1) Choose an unused stereo return, or two open channels on the console.

2) Lower the return levels.

3) Patch from the mono output of send 3 into the mono input of the digital reverb, then patch 2 cords out of the digital reverb stereo outputs, and into the chosen returns.

4) Pan the channels hard L and R. Check that master send level 3 is at a proper level, then raise the level of the send on any channel, say, the snare drum, and check the input levels on the reverb. If the input levels appear good, raise the level of the returns on the console for a split second. Not loud enough or long enough to distract the engineer, but enough to hear if the returns are working.

If the setup is correct, leave the send and returns off until the engineer needs them. He won't want to hear the additional hiss from any effects returns that he isn't using.

- Don't root around in the patchbay while any machine is in *record*. Dirty patchcord connections may create crackles on the recording. Wait until the multitrack is out of *record* to make a quick patch change.

- Don't patch out of a channel while that channel is in *record*. Even if your studio is properly wired and grounded, the output patch can load down the signal, lowering the *record* input level.

- As was mentioned earlier, patch in the direction of the signal flow. For example, to patch a limiter and equalizer across a channel insert, patch from the channel insert send into the input of the limiter, then out of the limiter and into the input of the equalizer, then finally back into the channel insert return.

    Because insert send points are half normal and insert return points are full normal, starting the patch at the insert returns creates a deadpatch. This channel is then dead until the rest of the patch is complete. If you follow the signal flow from the channel insert send, the patch returning into the channel insert return interrupts the signal not with dead space, but with the processed signal.

- Confirm that all patches will work. For example, the engineer wants to send the snare channel to an echo chamber, using buss 12 as the send. Notice the bussing on Figure 2.3, the input/setup sheet. Any channel bussed to track 12 will be recorded on track 12, which is one of the ambiance tracks. Tell him, and mention that buss 13 is available. Make the patch and, because the buss is normalled into track 13 on the recording machines, switch track 13 out of *record-ready*, or deadpatch the input. Professional consoles have a master buss level for each buss. In this example, channel 13 on the console will house the master buss level control.

- After the patch is complete, give the engineer a slight confirmation, with maybe a nod. Label the unit with a piece of white adhesive tape stating the send and return. If the engineer hasn't done so, write the send and return information on the scribble strip clearly and legibly. Fill in the strip how he does it. For example, if he uses red and blue markers, then you do the same.

- If the engineer writes something on the scribble strip, such as sends and returns, don't wait until he asks you to make the patches. Read what he has written, and make them.

- After working with the engineer you will learn how he uses certain pieces of equipment. If you think you know where he is going with something, set it up before he asks. For example, if he labels stereo return 4 with "send 4 into delay unit 3, then into echo chamber 4" you should realize his intention without him having to tell you. He probably wants a pre-delay on echo plate 4. A pre-delay is a delay inserted into the send of an analog echo plate.

    Check that the delay unit is switched on and the gain isn't too loud before making the patch. Remove the feedback, and set the length of the delay at around 40ms. He will adjust as needed.

- When the engineer makes a patch, go over and check to see that he made the patch correctly. When necessary, as in mixing, write the patch down to keep track of the sound. If you feel he patched something incorrectly or you don't understand a patch that he made, ask him about it at a convenient time.

RECORDING BASIC TRACKS

Now everything is ready to go. The digital recording machines, either open reel or DAW, are properly loaded, in *record-ready* mode and their operating parameters have been confirmed. Equipment setup and signal flow are complete, the musicians are comfortable and ready to play, and the engineer and producer are satisfied with the sounds.

As the players run through the song, scan the rooms to confirm that everything is as it should be, including all input and output meters, bussing, sends and returns and outboard equipment.

RUNNING THE RECORDER

In the early days of recording, multitrack tape machines had no remote controls, so the assistant engineer would stay next to the machines and run them throughout the session. Today, with the machine remote control close to, or even within the console, it might be more convenient for the engineer to operate it himself. Some engineers still expect the assistant to do all the recording, including punch-ins (going in and out of *record* at exact spots.)

With the ease of digital recording and editing, some engineers find it easier to record a song a few times, they then edit the choice pieces together for a master take. Some engineers prefer to punch in and out on an established master take. Whether you are recording to DAW or a digital open reel machine, your job is to—

- Completely understand the concept of the tape machine's record and playback section and their functions, the transport section, the meters and all parameter settings. If something is improperly set, such as an incorrect sampling rate, the whole session may go by without it being noticed.

- Record a tuning tone, commonly A-440. Occasionally, after the basics are complete, the client wants to slightly change the tempo of a song. Changes to the speed of the open reel machine also changes the tempo and tuning of the recorded music. As the pitch of the musical instruments on tape is changed, so is the pitch of the tuning tone. This tone is used to re-calibrate the tuner. The players then plug in to the tuner, and tune their instruments to the new pitch. Tempo and tuning are independent of each other on the DAW.

This tone is useful for tuning, but also helpful for when slaves are taken elsewhere. If the file is opened on a different DAW, incorrect clocking in the session setup may cause slight tempo and tuning changes. Run the tone through the tuner to confirm.

- Confirm that the multitrack is ready to *record*. As the musicians run through the song to get the feel of it, most engineers will want to record this first pass. Players with less studio experience may be more relaxed during the run through if they think they aren't being recorded. In my experience, this first pass can be the best.

- Watch the meters on the console when the multitrack in *record*. Also watch the multitrack's input levels, and any limiters and compressors. As musicians get into a song, they may play their instruments harder than when they played for the sound check. If any meters are hitting the red, or if a meter shows an overloaded signal, tell the engineer.

- Visually scan every multitrack VU meter to confirm that the correct signal is being recorded on the intended track. For example, if you see a continuous tone-like signal going to the snare drum track, you know something is wrong. Listen to the various instruments as you watch the input meters.

- Load a DAT or CD recorder, and press *record-ready*. Bands tend to jam, kid around, rehearse, and come up with new ideas between takes. It may be inconvenient to record these ideas to the main multitrack. With a CD or DAT cued up, these spontaneous ideas and meanderings can be instantly recorded.

- Wait until the engineer tells you to stop recording. You don't want to be guilty of pressing the stop button during a very quiet part in the middle of a song, or before the final chord of a song has finished ringing out.

- Once the song is complete and properly saved on the DAW, create a new *Song Title—Master* file from the template for the next song. This is just one method. Maybe the engineer wants to record the songs one after the other in one large file. This allows the plug-ins and processing to stay the same for all the songs. The engineer's way is the right way.

TRACKSHEETS

Figures 8.1 and 8.2 show that tracksheets are updated hard copy versions of what is recorded on each song. This allows anyone, at any time, to keep track of the progression of the sessions.

PROJECT INFORMATION

The project information is found at the top of the tracksheet and includes the song title, the artist or band, the producer, the engineer, the client, and the assistant engineer. The assistant's name is included so anyone else who works on the project with questions or problems will know who to contact. And remember, nobody likes to see their name spelled incorrectly.

This section also indicates how the song file is set up, including the host computer and its operating system, DAW program and software version, sample rate and bit depth, varispeed (if any), file format, the beats per minute of the song, and whether it is a digital master, slave or clone. All studios have their own similar style of tracksheet. Whatever sort of tracksheet you or your studio use—

- Make one sheet for each song.

- Write the tracks in pencil, not pen, as they may be modified, bounced, or simply erased or deleted.

- Log the track information during the recording, not before.

- Make sure the track sheet is always correct.

DAW TRACKSHEET/RECORDING MAP

Why use a tracksheet for a DAW when all the information is clearly visible in the mix window? Track sheets are a great resource for organization, especially as a project grows. They are a necessity when large files are sent to another studio for other engineers, so they can confirm that all the tracks in the DAW window match the tracksheet. Or when the producer just wants to flip through all the songs to see the progress of the project.

Some engineers may feel they do not need a tracksheet, and that is fine. Maybe smaller sessions don't need it. But a tracksheet or takesheet can also be use as a recording map for notes of tracks recorded.

Every DAW track has multiple playlists, or layers. These layers allow the user freedom to try different ideas. For example, he may use many layers on a vocal track to try a few editing ideas. If the session has three vocal tracks, each with 10 or 12 layers of vocal ideas, the engineer may use a recording map to keep track of choice bits within these layers.

In the digital recording studio, a recording map is used to keep track of copies, signal sources, transfers, track layers and other actions and resources not associated with analog recording.

Because DAW tracks are shifted up and down on a regular basis, the standard "guitar is always on track 12" concept is somewhat obsolete. The guitar is on whatever track is chosen at any given time. Still, most engineers prefer to lay their tracks out in a certain order to keep sessions unified and organized. Once the basic tracks are established, all of the songs on the project should be laid out similarly. On a DAW tracksheet, a simple list of tracks is usually all that is necessary. On the tracksheet—

- List the instrument, the part, and any basic information about the individual track. You normally won't need to include details such as microphone settings or studio used, just the basic track information. Those details are logged on the instrument set-up sheet.

```
DAW TRACKSHEET / RECORDING MAP

Title    _Macaroni and Cheese_____        Date    _July 29_____
Artist   _Tuff Beans_____        Client  _Crapitol Records_
Producer _Bob Loblaw_____        Studio  ☐ A  ☒ B  ☐ C
Engineer _Casey Jones_____        Assistant _A. Reader____
```

DAW INFORMATION

DAW Platform ☒ Mac ☐ PC ☐ Other		DAW Program _Pro-tools_
Host Computer _____ Host Computer OS _Jupiter_		Software Version _16.6_

Bit Depth		Sample Rate	
☐ 16		☐ 44.1 ☐ 88.2 ☐ 192	
☒ 24 Other _____		☒ 48 ☐ 96 ☐ Other ____	

Time Code Format	☐ 30	☐ 29.97 NDF	☐ 24	☐ SMPTE	Sync Ref (For master)
				☐ EBU	
	☐ 25	☐ 29.97 DF		☐ MTC	

File Format ☐ BWAV ☐ AIFF ☒ WAV ☐ MP3 ☐ OTHER _____

Sync Source _____   Hard Disc _____   Notes _____

Plug ins _____

General Tracking Notes

1	Talkback	15	Rhythm Guitar
2	Bass Guitar Amp	16	Guitar 2
3	Bass Guitar Direct	19	Keyboard L
4	Kick Drum	20	Keyboard R
5	Snare Drum	21	Reference Vocal
6	High Hat	23	Click/120 BPM
7	Tom-toms Low		
8	Tom-toms High		
9	Cymbals L		
10	Cymbals R		
11	Room Ambiance L		
12	Room Ambiance R		

Figure 8.1 DAW Tracksheet

- Write the track exactly as it is written on the DAW. Both the DAW file and the tracksheet must match. Don't rename or alter a track without first confirming with the engineer.

- Use a felt pen to draw a line on the tracksheet using the same color code. For example, if two bass guitar tracks are colored blue, then draw a blue line next to the two bass tracks on the tracksheet.

- If needed, the DAW tracksheet can double as a takesheet. Or even a page to jot down numbers, tracks, reminders, etc. Just add the date. A properly dated sheet of notes is better than a pile of scrap paper with a bunch of notes.

Once the master track is established, take a few moments to burn a backup, whether to a separate hard drive or Blu-Ray or other preferred storage method. Confirm that the size of the backup file is the same size as the original file, and that all paperwork is complete and correct. Finally, open the copy file to check that all is correct. Note that many DAW programs allow the user to create, update, and print tracksheets.

OPEN REEL TRACKSHEET

The traditional 24-track tracksheets have large blocks of space for all the track information such as instrument, part, microphone used, date recorded, and musician. Each track should include:

- The instrument. Sometimes just writing *keyboard* or *guitar* isn't enough. Write the complete name of the instrument, for example *Emulator 3 Grand Piano #2* or *'59 Fender Acoustic*.

- The part. Write down the complete part, such as *high rhythm*, or *low harmony 1*. Additionally, notice that in Figure 8.2, tracks 19 and 20 are in stereo, but tracks 15 and 17 are not, although they are the same part. Track 17 is labeled *with 15* and not *L* or *R*.

TITLE:	It's over, Flo
ARTIST:	Tuff Beans
PRODUCER:	Bob Loblaw
ENGINEER:	Casey Jones
CLIENT:	Crapitol Records

☐ 48 TK   ☐ 32 TK   ☒ 24 TK   ☐ 16 TK   ☐ 8 TK

1 *Talkback*	2 *Bass guitar* *amplifier*	3 *Bass guitar* *direct*	4 *Kick drum*
DATE: MIC:	DATE: MIC: *U 47*	DATE: MIC: *di*	DATE: MIC: *421*
ENG: STUDIO:	ENG: STUDIO:	ENG: STUDIO:	ENG: STUDIO:

9 ← *Cymbals* →	10	11 ← *Room ambiance* →	12
ride cymbal			
DATE: MIC: *U 87*	DATE: MIC: *U 87*	DATE: MIC: *414*	DATE: MIC: *414*
ENG: STUDIO:	ENG: STUDIO:	ENG: STUDIO:	ENG: STUDIO:

17 *Rhythm guitar* *'59 strat* *intro & choruses / dbl of 15* *acous guitar overdub* *verses 7/30 U 87*	18 *Lead vocal* ★	19 ← *Keyboards* → *korg / yamaha* L	20 R
DATE: MIC:	DATE: MIC: *U 87*	DATE: MIC: *di*	DATE: MIC: *di*
ENG: STUDIO:	ENG: STUDIO:	ENG: STUDIO:	ENG: STUDIO:

Figure 8.2 *Open Reel Tracksheet*

- Internal location. As the tracksheet fills up, additional space may be needed. A lack of available tracks might mean using one track for more than one instrument. The guitar on track 15 happens only in the intro and choruses of the song. This leaves space during the verses. Notice on the tracksheet that a tambourine was recorded as an overdub on track 15.

158

DATE: *July 29*	TAPE: *999*	SPEED: ☐ 30 IPS ☐ 15 IPS ☒ DIGITAL
STUDIO: ☐ A ☒ B ☐ C	N. R.: ☐ DOLBY ☐ DBX ☐ _____
REEL: *3* OF: *3*	SAMPLING RATE: ☒ 48 K ☐ 44.1 K
TONES ON REEL_____ ☐ HEAD ☐ TAIL	BIT DEPTH ☐ 16 ☒ 24 ☐ OTHER
ASSISTANT ENGINEER: *A. Reader*	

☐ 4 TK   ☒ MASTER   ☐ SAFETY   ☐ SLAVE   ☐ CLONE

5 *Snare drum*	6 *High hat*	7 ← *Tom toms* 8 →
		low *mid* *high*
DATE: / MIC: *57 / 451*	DATE: / MIC: *451*	DATE: MIC: *421* / DATE: MIC: *421*
ENG: / STUDIO:	ENG: / STUDIO:	ENG: STUDIO: / ENG: STUDIO:
13 *Vocal* work track # 1 overdub	14 *Vocal* work track # 2 overdub	15 *Rhythm guitar* '62 Les Paul intro & choruses / dbl of 17 tamborine overdub verses 7/30 / 16 *Guitar 2* telecaster
DATE: *7 / 30* MIC: *U 87*	DATE: *7 / 30* MIC: *U 87*	DATE: MIC: *421 / di* / DATE: MIC: *sm 57*
ENG: STUDIO:	ENG: STUDIO:	ENG: STUDIO: / ENG: STUDIO:
21	22 *Acoustic guitar 2* overdub	23 *Click track* 120 bpm / 24 *SMPTE* timecode / 30 FPS
DATE: MIC:	DATE: *7 / 30* MIC: *U 87*	DATE: MIC: / DATE: MIC:
ENG: STUDIO:	ENG: STUDIO:	ENG: STUDIO: / ENG: STUDIO:

- Musician. The musician's name might be written down only if there is more than one person playing a similar instrument. As in labelling the scribble strip, three guitar players would each have their names written on the tracks they played. One saxophone player wouldn't.

- Date. Write the recording date of every overdub for cross referencing your setup sheets and daily log. If there is no date written on the individual track, it is a basic track, and hasn't been updated. Of course, if everything is recorded in one day, there is no need to write down the recording date for all overdubs.

- Origin. If the track is a copy, a sample or bounce from another track, note its origin. Tracks are bounced within a master, from master to slave, and from slave to master. If the track is not from the basic session, mark OD, for overdub, on it. Notice on the tracksheet which tracks are from the basic, and which are overdubs.

- Suggestions and reminders. Note any ideas or reminders, such as specific panning or effects the engineer wants to remember for the mixing go here.

- Content. Some tracks may be kept strictly for reference, and are not meant for use in the final mix, such as the guide vocal on track 21. This track will probably be used until the final choice vocal track is completed, then deleted. Some tracks are recorded as work tracks, also called *feeders* or *source* tracks, and used to make one choice compilation track. Then, once the choice vocal track is established, it may be marked with a star using a red felt pen. Hide or delete these now obsolete feeder tracks.

- Engineer and studio. When more than one engineer is included, write each engineer's name on the tracks he recorded, and at what studio.

- Signal information. The microphones, limiters, and equalizers used during recording are sometimes also noted, though this information should appear on the setup sheet. (See Chapter Nine for more on setup sheets.)

Everything on the tracksheet must be accurate, legible, and current. Store the tracksheets in one of two places: on or near the console where the engineer can easily reach it, or if not in use, in the box with the multitrack tape. The assistant engineer is responsible for making sure all pertinent information for organization purposes is included.

TAKESHEETS

In the studio, a take is a recording of a musical or spoken piece. The players play the music and the engineer records it. Sometimes the best take is the first, and sometimes it's the twentieth. Takesheets, such as Figure 8.3 are used to map recorded performances, whether complete or incomplete, and to note any specific comments by the producer or engineer.

PROJECT INFORMATION

Because all of the technical information is available on the tracksheets and the tape labels, the project information found at the top of the tracksheet includes only the date, client, studio used, song title, the artist or band, the producer, the engineer, and the assistant engineer.

TITLES AND LOCATIONS

During the session, logging the takes and their locations has priority over almost everything. Too much time can be lost trying to make up for poor or incorrect documentation. This section includes—

- Titles. It's pretty obvious what goes here; the song title or musical part.

- Take. This shows the number of the take. If used, slate numbers must be consistent. Slate is when the engineer says "take 1" at the beginning of the pass. If a take is slated with a wrong number, such as take 2 being called take 3, either tell the engineer and he will slate the take again, or add a clear explanation on the takesheet. Time and energy may be wasted later hunting around for a nonexistent take 2.

- Locate. This section shows how long each take is. The numbers that show where a take starts and stops may not reveal a song's exact time. The engineer will record for a few moments before the song actually starts. Use the machine's counter to track specific locations.

TAKESHEET / RECORDING MAP

Title: _Macaroni and Cheese_   Date _July 29, Year_

Artist _Tuff Beans_   Client _Crapitol Records_

Producer _Bob Loblaw_   Studio ☐ A ☒ B ☐ C

Engineer _Casey Jones_   Assistant _A Reader_

TITLES	TAKE	LOCATE	COMMENTS
Macaroni and Cheese	_1_	_1:20_	_CT not tight_
	_2_	_5:30_	_inc._
	_(3)_	_9:30_	_CT Choice_
	_4_	_14:30_	_inc._
	_5_	_16:30_	_CT faster_
		_20:20_	_band chatter_
	_6_	_25:30_	_FS_
	_7_	_28:00_	_CT long intro_

FS - FALSE START	CT - COMPLETE TAKE	INC - INCOMPLETE TAKE	CH - CHOICE

Figure 8.3 _Takesheet/Recording Map_

- Comments. The comments section shows the status of each numbered take using the codes at the bottom of the takesheet. An FS label means a false start, CT means a complete take. INC means incomplete. Also ALT means alternate version, and CHOICE means.. well, you get the picture.

There are many more possibilities, but these are the most common. Additionally, general comments by the producer or engineer, such as "good choruses" or "great ending" are noted to help everyone remember the best parts. Mark these comments down even if they aren't speaking directly to you, like when the producer tells the engineer about a take or section of a take he prefers.

OPEN REEL LABELS

As stressed throughout this book, proper labelling is paramount. Figure 8.4 shows a typical tape label. It can be used for all tapes, including master tapes, slave tapes, mix tapes, outtake tapes, copy tapes, sample tapes, and back-up tapes. Write all labels with felt pen, not regular pen, and definitely not pencil.

The project information section includes the artist or band, the producer, the engineer, the client, and the assistant engineer. This section also indicates how the reel is set up, including the sample rate and bit depth, varispeed, time code format, BPM, and whether it is a digital master, slave or clone, and studio used.

The project information section on the tape label is the same as on the tracksheet label, including the date, artist, producer, engineer, assistant engineer, client, studio used and technical details.

Date							
7 29	DIGITAL REEL LABEL						
	Artist __Tuff Beans__				Date __July 29, Year__		
	Producer __Bob Loblaw__				Client __Crapitol Records__		
Artist	Engineer __Casey Jones__				Studio ☐ A ☒ B ☐ C		
TUFF BEANS	Assistant __A Reader__				Reel __2__ of __5__		

DIGITAL MACHINE INFORMATION
Digital Machine ___3348___ Tracks ___48___   Tape Speed _____

Bit Depth	☐ 16		Sample Rate	☐ 44.1 ☐ 88.2 ☐ 192
	☒ 24 Other ____			☒ 48 ☐ 96 ☐ ____
Time Code Format	☐ 30 ☒ 29.97 NDF ☐ 24		☒ SMPTE	Sync Ref (For master)
			☐ EBU	
	☐ 25 ☐ 29.97 DF		☐ MTC	

TITLES	TAKE	LOCATE	COMMENTS
Macaroni and Cheese	1	1:20	Loose
	(3)	9:30	Choice
	5	16:30	Faster
	7	28:00	Long intro
Its over, Flo	(1)	29:20	CT Choice
	3	33:20	CT Sluggish
Tuning tone A-440		35:30	:25 seconds

Left margin column: Titles — Mac and Cheese / It's Over Flo; Reel 2 of 5; Library

Figure 8.4 *Tape Label*

TITLES AND LOCATIONS

The title section of the label may seem like it holds the same information as the title section of the takesheet. Not so. Takesheets are used to organize passes and sections of a song before editing and assembly. Only the final edited versions are written on the label.

You can always write some labels beforehand with all the project information noted. Then, during the session, all that needs to be added is—

- The song titles and locations, plus any notes or comments.

- The location and level of any alignment tones and record pad, track format, and any varispeed or noise reduction.

- Numbers for reference and storage. When the project is using only four or five reels, organization will be easy. Larger projects might have a variety of formats. All tapes and recording media must be numbered and organized for quick and easy access. (See Chapter Twelve for more on tape control numbers.)

SPINE

The information on the spine in Figure 8.4 includes the date, artist, titles, master and slave information for each song, and a reference number. Reels, hard drives, and discs in the vault are stored like shelves of books, so there must be enough information on the spines to differentiate one from another.

When not in use, store the takesheets, tracksheets, session notes, and any other paperwork with the rest of the tapes and media.

LABELLING THE REEL

Figure 8.5 shows that labelling the reel makes things convenient when locating songs. All reels look the same once they are out of the box, so each reel should be labeled with the project, reel number and content.

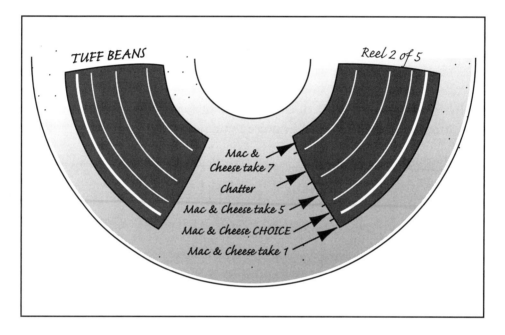

Figure 8.5 *Labelling the Reel*

CUES

Save a clean legible copy of the lyrics and a pencil for the engineer. He may want to write down line numbers for easier punches. When you have the final version of any lyrics, photocopy the page, and keep a copy in the daily log. Don't use a three-hole punch on original lyrics, only the copies. Date all lyrics to organize updated versions. Once the choice version is established, set location markers at every four or eight bars, or at specific changes within the song structure, such as the intro, verses or choruses.

Sheet music is used mainly when recording jingles, ensembles, and of course, orchestrations. It's not commonly used in pop or rock and roll. If your session uses sheet music, during the mayhem of recording, try to read along with the music and the cues. The ability to read music is an asset for any recording engineer.

	Drums	Bass	Gtr 1	Gtr 2	Ld Gtr	Kbds	Voc 1	Voc 2	Done
Party, party, party...									√
Too tuff to tame									√
Wiener water soup blues									
Fort McMurray Stomp									
It's over, Flo									√
Lost in Chinatown									
Macaroni and Cheese									
Joe Perry's Guitar									√
Where the flies are									
Travel in black									

Figure 8.6 Progress Chart

PROGRESS CHART

Some producers and engineers find it helpful to keep a progress chart on the wall of the control room. Figure 8.6 shows a chart displaying ten songs in various degrees of completion. As each instrument is recorded, half of the corresponding square is filled in. When that track is tightened, meaning edited and cleaned, the other half of the square is filled in, meaning the track is complete. In songs without the listed instrument, the square is simply crossed off.

For vocals, note how each square is split into three sections. The first section shows if the vocal has been recorded. The second section shows whether that vocal has been or comped, and the third section tells whether the vocal has been tuned. (See Chapter Ten for more on comping vocals.)

See that "Where the flies are" has the drums, bass, guitar and reference vocal recorded but not tightened. Maybe this song was recorded during basics, then abandoned.

The chart also shows that "It's over, Flo'" has drums, bass and all guitars recorded and tightened. Plus the vocals have all been recorded, tightened, and tuned. The check mark in the last square to the right shows that this song is ready to be mixed. With this chart, anyone can look across the room and see what tracks have been recorded and what is needed to complete the project.

. . . .

Summary

Chapter Eight explained what is expected of the assistant engineer during the recording of basic tracks:

- Making any changes, including microphones and their parameters, cables, and patches and headphones before the recording starts.

- Keeping track of cues as the basic tracks are recorded.

- Running all the machines as the "tape operator."

- Keeping track of all paperwork, including takesheets, tape labels, labelling everything, and updating the progress chart.

CHAPTER NINE

. . . .

After Basic Tracks

When the producer feels there is enough music recorded for a master take of a song, he might ask the musicians to come in from the studio and listen to each take to express their opinion. Although this determination is usually the producer's domain, most producers will respect a musician's input. If the musicians are hired guns they will play the part until the producer is satisfied, with minimal input regarding choices of takes.

The producer will tell you which take he wants to hear first. Switch all tracks on the multitrack out of *record-ready*, then cue up the correct take. They do not want to hear take 1 when they ask to hear take 2. Neither do they want to hear false starts. Wait until everyone is in the room before pressing play.

When all the musicians are in the control room listening, give one of them the engineer's chair. As they listen back to all the takes, you may want to sneak out to the studio and clean up coffee cups, ashtrays, cables, and anything else out of place. If the engineer wants to hear another take, or a section of another take while you're in the studio, he should be able to locate it using the machine counter locate numbers written on the takesheet. As you clean up, listen to the music through the headphones strewn throughout the studio. When the song is almost over, return to the control room, in case anyone needs anything.

After all the takes have been heard, take note if anyone states a preference. Later in the session, after doing many more takes, someone will undoubtedly wonder which was the early favorite. When everyone agrees that the performances recorded are enough to work with, the producer may want to do any number of things.

EDITS

Most songs you hear today are a combination of many different takes. A song will be recorded many times, using the same tempo and structure. On traditional analog 2" tape, the engineer would edit together a choice version of the song containing all the best parts from all the passes. He would physically cut the analog tape with a razor blade, then insert another section so as to seem seamless in the song.

For example, he may use the first chorus from take 2, the second chorus from take 4, the verses from take 3, and combine them all to create one final choice take. The band may also play the song different ways, perhaps with different endings, then wait to hear the edited takes before deciding which version is best.

Whether the edits are analog or digital, they will either be insert edits, or assembly edits. Insert edits involve replacing unsatisfactory sections, for example replacing one chorus with a better chorus from another take or even from elsewhere in the song. Assembly edits involve building the song from the beginning with the best sections of all the takes. Some songs are edited simply because they are too long.

Some producers never edit the song at the multitrack stage as they feel editing may take some of the magic away from the flow of the song. Jingles are rarely edited at the multitrack stage. Often they are written and recorded exactly 15, 30 or 60 seconds long for radio and TV spots, and editing them would change their exact timing. Editing takes time, and jingle sessions are always on a tight schedule. Most jingle edits take place during mixdown, when shorter or longer versions of a spot are needed.

When open reel digital tape is edited, these edits must be exact. The person doing the edits should wear gloves to avoid contamination—as the tape must remain clean, and the edits must be perfect. Of course, on a DAW editing is a basic feature. Open reel digital editing has almost disappeared in today's recording studio.

On many of today's sessions, the producer will have the engineer record the whole band, but concentrate on the drums sounding right. Once the best is recorded, the engineer may edit the best pieces together for a choice drum track. After the drum edits, certain spots on other tracks, such as the bass and guitars, may not flow over the edits smoothly. These spots, and any other spots that aren't acceptable, will need to be repaired or even completely re-done. Once the basic track is recorded, and the producer is happy with the engineer's edits—

- Go through the edited tracks and remove all clicks and pops using the *auto region fade in/out* feature. Fix any errant crossfades so every join is unnoticeable.

- Paste a copy of the track to a new layer. Correctly label the layer, then consolidate the copy. This is now your master track. Consolidating combines the many edited regions into one region. Don't consolidate a track too many times, or you risk signal degradation.

- Think before deleting regions from the playlist. It's better to just remove, or clear them, because deleting erases these regions from the hard drive. Removing them means they are still on the hard drive, just not in the playlist. Some engineers may want you to remove all these unconsolidated regions from the playlist, and some may want them left in. Delete only when you are sure, and even then, make a safety copy first.

REPAIRS

Before starting the repairs, switch all tracks on the multitrack out of *record-ready* except the tracks to be worked on. If additional tracks are recorded, these cease to be repairs, and become overdubs.

MUSICIAN IN THE STUDIO

When a musician must repair a track, the rest of the musicians may leave the studio. As they do, go out into the studio and unplug all their headphones. Signal blaring through all the headphones will be picked up by the active microphones. Don't change the volume on the headphone boxes, as they are set to where each musician wants them for the next song. If there is any unwanted noise, such as buzzing amplifiers or rattling snares, check with the engineer before eliminating it.

MUSICIAN IN THE CONTROL ROOM

When recording an electric instrument, such as an amplified guitar, the player may prefer to leave the studio and play in the control room. Even though the player moves, the sound must stay the same for continuity when punching in and out of the existing track, so the amplifiers remain where they are. As the sound doesn't emanate acoustically from the instrument, the engineer would only hear the output of amplifier through the microphones. The cables on the instrument may need extending as the player moves from the studio to the control room.

The musician playing in the control room may choose not to use headphones, since the music will be pumping through the main speakers during the repair. The only disadvantage here is for the engineer. He needs to hear everything from his own perspective, maybe soloing tracks to listen for various things. If the musician is using the main speakers for his cue, the engineer must monitor the song to the musician's wants and needs. If the musician wants more bass, the engineer must turn up the bass.

Also, the musician must be positioned where he can hear the speakers in a comfortable spot. If he is all the way over on one side of the room, he may not feel the impact of the song as he would if he were in the middle of the stereo spectrum. Some studios have extra speakers for musicians to use while playing in the control room.

INSTRUMENT SETUP SHEETS

Use the setup sheet to write down the instrument, its placement in the studio and its settings, the microphones and their parameters, the inputs on the console, the signal processing, the bussing, the patching, and the tracks being recorded. Once the sound is documented, the exact same sound can hopefully be recreated at any time in the future. There are many reasons a sound is documented.

- After spending most of a session getting a good sound, time runs out before the part is recorded correctly. The producer wants to start the next session with the same sound, and continue recording.

- The producer may be very happy with a sound recorded, and wants to use the same sound later on a different song.

- If a part in the song is changed later in the project, or section of a track is accidentally erased, the sound can be set up exactly as before, and the track can be repaired.

CREATING AND DOCUMENTING

To log the settings on equipment quickly and accurately, use a setup sheet, such as Figure 9.1. Because there is no standard method of writing down a setup, one specific sheet cannot cover all the different options. Many equipment manuals include master sheets of equipment faceplates. Photocopy the pages, showing the faceplates, and leaving enough space on the sheet for logging the internal settings. Your studio may already have these copies.

173

If there are no master sheets, draw them up yourself, making sure they are accurate. Sometimes reproductions of the faceplates are not needed. If the settings on a certain unit can be written using numbers, use a plain sheet of paper to write the setup. Again, your studio procedure dictates. Some studios have master templates on the hard drive, ready to be printed.

Document everything clearly and precisely. Sometimes a digital camera is used to capture exact placements. The setup sheet should include:

- Date. Clearly write the date of each recording for cross referencing. Anyone should be able to look at the tracksheet, refer to the corresponding date in the log, find the setup sheet, and access any information regarding the sound and setup.

- Track information. The band or artist's name, the song title, the individual track numbers and location of the sound within the song must appear. Figure 8.2 shows some tracks have more than one instrument at different sections, such as track 15.

- Instrument. Write the name and model of the instrument used, including its settings, any specific tuning, knob settings, switches, and if possible, the apparent age and gauge of any strings used. If necessary, note the musician's name as well.

- Effects. Effects boxes, their settings, whether on or off during the performance, the order in which they appear, battery or AC powered, and anything else that might affect the audio signal must be logged.

- Amplification. Include the placement and identity of the amplifier, the settings of the knobs, the specific input used, and any relevant amplifier information, such as installation of special tubes or cards. Show the sheet to the musician to see if anything has been overlooked.

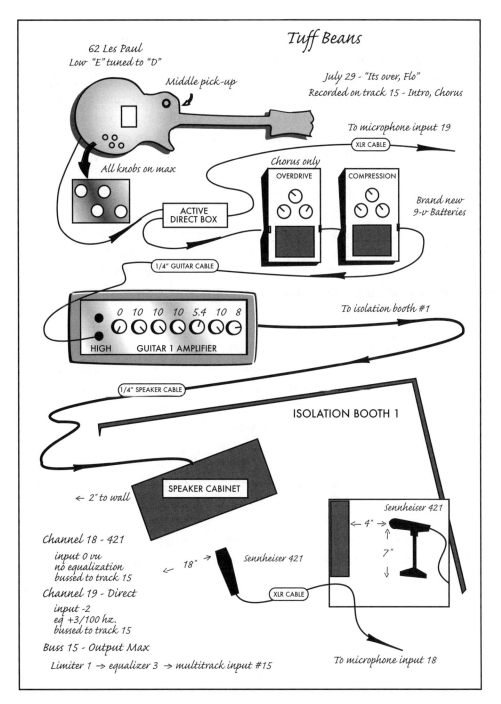

Figure 9.1 Setup Sheet

- Microphones and placement. Note the microphone's make, model, serial number, exact placement, respective pads and polar patterns. If you are returning to the same sound next session, but can't leave the equipment set up, use white adhesive tape on the floor to show precise placement of the microphones and amplifiers. Label the adhesive tape with the date, song title, and part. If you aren't planning to return to the sound in the very near future, adhesive tape on the floor won't last very long.

- Console and inputs. The inputs to the console, the line/microphone level, any equalization and limiting, individual channel fader levels, bussing, and patching must be logged. Most engineers want to use the same channels for repairs as used for the original recording. Better consoles tend to have a computer to store and recall these settings, so store all console settings, then confirm and properly label the settings.

- Outboard. Figure 9.2 shows part of the setup sheet. Write down all outboard equipment settings, both internal and external, front and rear, including the inputs and outputs used. If the studio owns more than one unit of the same model, note the one used. If using rental equipment, write down the make and serial number of the unit, and the rental company. The engineer will definitely want the same unit when re-doing the setup.

    When any processing, such as an equalizer or tube compressor is in the path but not active, include it in the setup sheet, stating its status. Although inactive, it may change the sound slightly.

Setup sheets must be clear and organized, as you may not be the person re-creating the setup. Once the setup is completely logged, go over the signal path one final time to confirm that the setup sheet is correct.

If time permits, write down every sound recorded, no matter how minor it may seem to you. If it isn't important, it wouldn't be there. For example, the producer leaves the session early, and a musician records a rough idea, just using a quick setup, and then moves on. Weeks later, the producer hears the part, loves it, and wants the musician to record it correctly, using the same sounds.

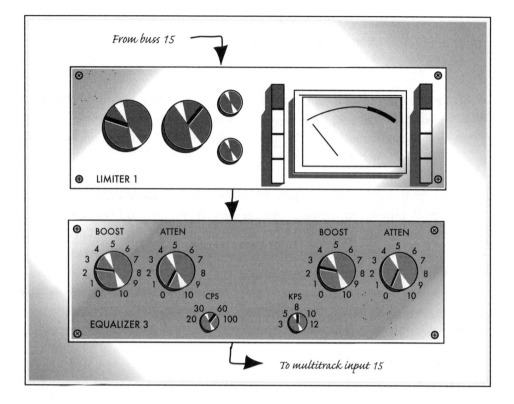

Figure 9.2 Outboard Setup

CLOSING THE DAW SESSION

Before closing the session and moving on —

- Either clear tracks no longer in use, or mute the voice and hide the track, so unused work tracks are no longer active or visible.

- Confirm that the mix window is laid out in a logical manner, such as the music tracks, then the master fader, then the effects returns. Or have the drums with their effects, the guitars with their effects, then the master fader. There is no right or wrong way, as long as the layout is properly organized and all sends and returns are clearly labelled.

- Confirm location markers at the appropriate spots within the song, such as the verse, chorus and guitar solo. Check that you are on the correct take.

- If necessary, create a tempo map of the song. When a song is recorded without a click track, the tempo will vary slightly throughout the song. A tempo map tracks these small changes to allow a sequencer to accurately follow the song tempo.

- Confirm that all tracks are properly labelled. Use the comment sections to detail sends, returns and settings of effects. For additional space to document settings, maybe create an adjacent MIDI track that allows the user to see the information along the time line in the *edit* window.

- Note the key of the song in the *session info* window.

- Go through and remove any obsolete or redundant tracks, files and playlists.

- Mute regions using *de-activate* rather than automation.

- Collect all paperwork and files from the previous song in an envelope, and place them where all the files will be housed. Include all lyrics, tracksheets, takesheets and notes.

FILE MANAGEMENT

Place the current *Song Title—Master* in its properly labelled folder, probably in the top level of the session folder. Place non-master files, such as work files or slaves in their own properly labelled files, yet still all within the *Master Session* folder. Make sure to set up folders for master sessions, source sessions, backup copies, rough mixes, final mixes and other edited/normalized/mastered mixes.

If your sessions are using more than one hard drive, clearly label which hard drive holds the current masters. Splitting files up, such as placing audio files on one hard drive, and fade files on another is asking for trouble.

LABELLING

Proper labelling and documentation is essential for ease of locating master files and avoiding confusion, especially when copies and clones of files are made and moved.

RECORDING BASIC TRACKS FOR ANOTHER SONG

As everyone returns to the studio for the next song's basic tracks—

• Make a copy of the master file, if needed, and relabel it to begin a new song. Properly label the copy as previously laid out. Switch all the tracks to *record-ready* mode.

• Remove the existing scribble strip of tape from the console and place it on the control room window for storage. Write the title of the song on the end piece of the strip. Replace the strip on the console with a new length of adhesive tape for the new song. If the track information is not written on adhesive tape, but written on the actual strip on the console, use the tracksheet to re-write the track information on the strip. Either way, the basic track information will most likely remain the same.

• Prepare a new tracksheet, takesheet or any other necessary paperwork.

• Confirm the VSO is switched off.

- If a click generator is used, you may need to change the tempo, after the old click tempo is noted. Confirm this with the engineer.

- As the musicians return to the studio to continue recording, go out with them and plug in all the headphones. Musicians love to put on headphones first, and then plug them in. This usually blasts their ear-drums—but they never learn.

- Help the musicians with any of their session needs. When everyone in the studio is ready, return to the control room and prepare for the next basic track.

ASSEMBLING MASTER MULTITRACK REELS

Choice takes that are scattered throughout many reels must be removed from their original reels, and placed on master reels. Master reels are reels that contain only the final choice passes. The number of these master reels can vary from just a few to many.

To assemble master open reels—

1) Find the reel with the first master take, and load it on the multitrack machine. Transport the tape to the beginning of the song.

2) Splice the tape at least 15 seconds before the count of the song. No tight leaders at this point in the project. Tight leadering is removing the count at the beginning, and leadering up to the start of the song.

3) Remove the original reel from the take-up side of the machine, and re-place it with the now empty Master Reel 1. Load it with a few feet of blank tape, splice in a length of leader tape, then splice the beginning of

the first song to the end of the leader. A splice is when you lay two pieces of tape, or a piece of tape and a leader in a splicing block, then use a sharp razor blade cut both pieces. The excess sections are removed, and the two retained pieces are edited together using splicing tape.

4) Use a felt pen to write the title of the song on the leader, so when the tape is parked at the beginning of a song, anyone can see which song is loaded.

5) Wind the reel to the end of the first master take, and splice in a leader, again leaving ample tape before the splice. Note that some engineers may disagree with adding leaders to digital tapes. Check first.

6) Remove the master reel from the take-up side of the machine, and load the original reel. Splice the ends together, and wind the reel off. This reel is now less one song.

7) Write "Pulled to Master," or simply PTM and the date on the box that originally held the master take. On the master reel box, state which reel the take came from, and the take number, if possible. Some choice takes might be edited combinations of many different takes.

8) Do the assembly so the splices can't be physically heard. Turn down the monitors, and listen to the tape crossing the heads. If you can hear a splice go by, stop tape, open the splice and re-do it. These splices may pass over the heads hundreds of times, and must be secure.

9) Find the reel that has the next song to be placed on the master reel, and load it on the machine. Repeat.

10) Continue until Master Reel 1 is full, then start over on Master Reel 2. Don't overload a master reel. Any alignment tones either have their own reel, or are placed at the end of the first reel.

Date	8 04 Year
Artist	TUFF BEANS
Titles	Too Tuff... / Night of... / Party, Party...
Reel	M1 of 2
Library	631.3 .4

DIGITAL REEL LABEL

Artist: Tuff Beans — Date: August 4, Year

Producer: Bob Loblaw — Client: Crapitol Records

Engineer: Casey Jones — Studio: ☐ A ☒ B ☐ C

Assistant: A Reader — Reel: M1 of 2

DIGITAL MACHINE INFORMATION

Digital Machine: 3348 — Tracks: 48 — Tape Speed: ______

Bit Depth: ☐ 16 ☒ 24 Other ______ — Sample Rate: ☐ 44.1 ☐ 88.2 ☐ 192 ☒ 48 ☐ 96 ☐ ______

Time Code Format: ☒ 30 ☐ 29.97 NDF ☐ 24 ☐ 25 ☐ 29.97 DF — ☒ SMPTE ☐ EBU ☐ MTC — Sync Ref (For master)

TITLES	TAKE	LOCATE	COMMENTS
MASTER REEL 1 OF 2			
Too Tuff To Tame	4	:20	HTL
Night of the Living Beans	1	5:45	TL
Party Party Party Party Party	-	9:30	TL
Tuning tone A= 440 Hz		14.10	

***Figure 9.3** Master Tape Label*

LABELLING

Every song must be clearly marked with exactly what is on it. Figure 9.3 shows how Reel 1 is labelled with—

- "Too Tuff to Tame" starting at 0:20, and is about 5 minutes long. Take 4 is being used as the master and is marked HTL, head and tail leadered.

- Then "Night of the Living Beans" starting at 5:45. Take 1 is the master and is marked TL, tail leadered. The tail leader of the previous song on the reel is this song's head leader.

- "Party, Party, Party, Party, Party," the last song on the reel starting at 9:30, and the take is not noted. This may mean that it is edited together from different takes. It is 5 minutes long, and also marked TL.

- A tuning tone placed at the end of the reel.

. . . .

Summary

Chapter Nine explained what is expected of the assistant engineer after the basic tracks are recorded:

- Helping the engineer create a master take with organization before, during and after the multitrack edits.

- Repairs of tracks recorded during the basics.

- Closing and saving the DAW session.

- Creating setup sheets, and documenting all sounds recorded.

- Assembling all the choice basic tracks.

- Organizing and managing song files.

10

CHAPTER TEN

. . . .

Recording Overdubs

The basic tracks are now recorded. The songs have all been edited using the best pieces to create the choice versions. The individual tracks that are being kept from the basic sessions have all been repaired, and everything that needs documenting has been properly labelled and logged. All songs have been properly assembled onto master reels or to master file sessions.

It is time to move from basics to overdubs. Overdubs are additional recordings added to a song after the basic tracks are complete, often one instrument at a time. Overdubs usually take the most hours in a large project, and can take weeks, months or even years on some projects.

When the engineer tells you what changes to make, write everything down in detail on your pad of paper so you don't have to ask a second time. If the engineer wants to record a vocal overdub on another song, using a Neumann U-87 in channel 25 on the console, with a limiter then an equalizer on the channel, and he wants to record it on track 13, you had better write that down.

FINDING THE SONG

Whenever moving to a new song and changing a setup, load the new song first, then set up the studio second. This way, the engineer can prepare a new setup and monitor mix, and the musician can hear the song while you set up the studio.

Many studios today use any combination of analog and digital formats, including open reel tapes, digital cassettes such as A-DAT, and/or DAW hard drive storage systems, all depending on what format the engineer wants, or what format incoming recordings are when they arrive at the session.

Some of the following may not be applicable. When changing open reels or digital cassettes to find and load another song, follow this procedure:

1) Disarm any tracks in *record-ready*.

2) Switch the machine to *input* to keep the microphones active. If the musicians stay in the studio during the changeover, the people in the control room might want to talk with them. You could also mute the output of the console, but this also mutes communication to and from the studio.

3) Wind the tape to the end of the reel. Digital tapes are stored heads out, and analog tapes are stored tails out. Place the collar around the reel, or use a small piece of adhesive tape to hold the end of the tape in place.

4) Find the tracksheet and check with the engineer to be sure that all updates have been noted. You may not have noticed that a track was modified or erased while you were doing something else.

5) If the VSO was used, note the new speed on the tracksheet, then deactivate it.

6) Remove the reel from the machine, place it in the correct box with the tracksheet, then put it with the rest of the tapes.

7) Gather the rest of the paperwork for the particular song. Again, when the collection of lyrics, setup sheets and notes becomes too large to keep with the daily log, store it in a large, clearly labeled manila envelope or a three-ring binder.

8) Find the tape containing the next song to be used, load it on the spindle, and thread it up. Return the head protector to its upright position. If noted on the tracksheet, set the VSO to the correct speed, leave it off, and ask the engineer when he wants it activated.

9) Open the new tracksheet, if there is one, and place it on the console facing the engineer.

10) Confirm that the intended track is open. If something is already recorded on the track, the engineer either doesn't realize it, or he wants to record additional instruments on the open areas. For example, Figure 8.2 shows that the guitar on track 15 occurs only in the intro and choruses. This leaves open space in the verses for a tambourine. As the two instruments never play simultaneously, they can occupy the same track.

11) If the song resides on a hard drive, open the file with the new song. If two files of the same name exist, open the one with the newer date, and place the older file in a properly labelled folder. Confirm that all plug-ins are activated.

12) Create and label a new track, set it to *record-ready*, and label it appropriately. Place the cursor at the top of the song. Depending on how the engineer prefers to work, he may set up a cue mix within the DAW or through the console. However he chooses is the correct way.

SETTING UP THE STUDIO

Now that the proper song is cued up and the parameters on the machine are set, the engineer can ready the console for the overdub while you ready the studio. Before a new setup is started, the old one is usually broken down, but in some cases, the setup is left intact. For example, if the engineer wants to use part of the setup again, or if the setup needs to be documented and there isn't time to do it between the changeover of songs.

The most common setup for a vocal or single instrument overdub is one microphone in the studio. This is not necessarily the only way, or even the right way. You will discover that there is no right or wrong way to record. According to your pad of paper, follow these steps:

1) Mute channel 13 on the console.

2) Go into the studio and lay out a small carpet. This eliminates the possibility of floor squeaks and toe taps being picked up by the microphone. Place the carpet where the musician can be seen from the control room.

3) You might want to set up two or three baffles behind the musician to minimize unwanted room ambiance.

4) Place the stand, then attach the microphone. Save time by using any stands and cables already set up. Connect the cables and headphones as described in Chapter Three.

5) Place a jug of water, or cup of tea with honey on a small table nearby. Keep them filled throughout the session. These are not only for refreshment, but to help ease the throat. During vocals, don't fill the water glass with ice cold water, as cold water can strain the vocal chords.

6) When a music stand is needed, place the appropriate lyrics or music, a sharpened pencil, and maybe a light on the stand. Draping a small towel over the stand absorbs the sound, keeping it from reflecting back into the microphone.

7) The musician may request a chair or stool to sit on.

8) On some recordings, a certain mood may be needed. Maybe the musician wants the lights down low to evoke a more creative atmosphere. Candles or incense can sometimes used to create a mood, although not always.

SETTING UP THE CONSOLE

Once the studio setup is complete, return to the control room to help prepare the console and patchbay. The engineer may prefer to set up the console himself, or he may let you do it. If any patches are needed, make the patches, document the patch on your pad of paper, then start setting a headphone cue mix for the musician.

CONSOLE STATUS

Depending on the engineer's preference, the console status may or may not stay the same for the overdub as it was for basics. Commonly, when all the basics are complete, the console status is switched so the main faders change from microphone inputs to multitrack returns.

When this change happens, channels must be re-zeroed so the signal processing used for the microphone inputs is not applied to the multitrack returns. For example, during basic tracks, when the console was in *microphone* status, the engineer set the equalization on channel 10, the high-hat. When the console is switched to *line* status, channel 10 has a cymbal track returning on it. This high-hat equalization, when left activated, is incorrectly applied to the cymbal.

SIGNAL ROUTING

Route the incoming microphone signal to the multitrack either through busses on the console, or through direct inputs at the patchbay.

Channel routing follows no rules. Many channels on the console might be routed to one track on the multitrack, or one channel might be routed to many tracks on the console. During basics, if the situation called for it, the engineer could buss all the microphones on the all instruments to one track, then buss one microphone from one guitar to the other twenty-three tracks for one long, loud, twenty-three-track guitar solo.

To route the signal according to the tracksheet, follow these steps:

1) Return to the control room and prepare channel 25 on the console, the input for the microphone. According to your pad of paper, track 13 is the intended track for the overdub.

2) Check that channel 25 on the console is not a channel the engineer wants to leave set up for future use.

3) Switch channel 25 from *line* to *microphone* status.

4) Remove any equalization, patches, or subgroups on channel 25. Lower all sends and, if applicable, activate the phantom power.

5) Switch track 13 to *record-ready*, which will switch the machine to *input* mode. The instrument to be recorded must be monitored for correct sound and input level. Press buss 13 on channel 25. This is not the only way to send the signal to the multitrack, but it is a common way. The engineer will tell you if he prefers a different method.

6) Patch in the limiting and equalization, deactivate the equalization from the signal, and set the limiter to a moderate level. The engineer will set them when necessary.

Depending on the engineer's preference, the limiting and equalization processing could be patched either before or after the buss. If this processing is patched before the buss output (out of the insert send, into the processing then back again into the insert return of the channel) the processed signal goes to all busses pressed on channel 25.

If the signal is patched after the buss (from the buss output into the limiting and equalization processing then back into the multitrack input), when the engineer wants to change tracks from 13 to record on track 14 you must change the patch from input 13 to input 14.

TESTING THE INPUTS

Once the console is set, check the input from the microphone for proper connection. Follow these steps:

1) At the console, un-mute channel 13. Slowly raise the level on channel 13 and, to hear if microphone input 25 is working, bring up the fader level of channel 25. When you hear the room noise in the studio being routed from the microphone through channel 25 to track 13, lower the main fader level on channel 13. Do not press the cut button.

2) On channel 13, set the cue send switch to *pre-fader* and raise the cue send level. This level is now independent of the main fader level. Raise the master cue send level just over half way.

3) Go into the studio, put on the headphones, and speak into the microphone. You should hear yourself in the headphones. The control room will not hear you because the main fader on channel 13 is lowered. The cut button on channel 13 is not pressed, as that may mute the microphone.

    If you can see the multitrack recorder from the studio, look at the input meter level on channel 13 as you speak into it. If the level needs adjusting, go into the control room and adjust it, then repeat the process. Do the same with the cue level.

4) Once the levels are set, add any reverbs or delays to the headphone mix. Go back out to the studio and check the headphones again. As you speak, listen to the reverb level. Is it loud enough? Is it in stereo? Can you hear everything? Set everything up so the musician can walk out, put on the headphones and begin.

REST OF THE CONSOLE

Before changing the console completely, check again that the engineer does not want to keep any of the existing channels set up. Though everything is documented, he may want to keep an instrument set up for later use.

To set the console up for overdubs —

- Don't zero the equalization on each channel, just deactivate it for now and deal with it when time allows.

- Lower all the faders, and remove any subgroups.

- Lower all the sends. Leave the master send and return levels alone, as they are still being used.

- Pull all the applicable patches, leaving the ones still in use, such as effects sends and returns.

- If the monitor source is being changed from the monitor section of the console to the main faders, change any applicable patches. For example, if multitrack return 8 on the monitor section has a limiter patched into it, remove the limiter from the monitor section and place it into the appropriate channel in the main monitor.

- The cue system may have its own echo plate. If so, patch this off an unused send so a musician can hear his echo in the headphones.

- When the session changes from one song to another, the adhesive scribble strip on the console needs to be updated with the new track layout. As basics are over, each song recorded should have its own strip somewhere in the control room.

SETTING UP A PREVIOUS SOUND

When the time comes to return to a sound that was documented earlier in the project, setup should be relatively easy if the original was correctly logged. If the equipment is still set up, especially if the microphones and amplifiers haven't been moved, the job of returning to the original sound is much easier. If the total setup has been broken down, you need to start from scratch. To return to a previous sound—

1) Check the tracksheet for the original recording date, go to that date in the daily log, and find the correct setup. If no date is written on the individual track, you know it was recorded during the basic.

2) Set up the instrument and microphones as detailed on the setup sheet (Figure 9.1). If possible, use the same outboard, channels and microphones that were used during the original recording.

3) After completing the setup, load the multitrack with the song containing the sound you are re-creating. Ask the musician to play along with the original, and A/B them. (Switch back and forth between the original sound recorded and the live sound being played.) The goal is to recreate the original sound. If there is a difference between the two sounds, trace the signal flow and re-check the setup sheet.

If the setup was correctly written down, the sound should be close. Realize that no matter how diligently the original was logged, the same sound just might not return. The engineer will realize this, and he will work with the new sound until it matches the old. He may simply use the existing sound setup as a starting point for a new sound.

If there are enough channels on the console, some channels might stay set up for the duration of the project, such as a vocal setup. Whenever the singer has the urge to record a track, he just walks out and sings without having to wait around while you set everything up.

MONITOR MIX

A monitor mix is a rough setting of all the levels, panning, and effects returning to the console, either live or from a multitrack. The monitor mix lets everyone in the control room hear what is being, and what has been, recorded.

If the engineer doesn't begin setting up a monitor mix, sit in the main chair and start. Bring up the levels of the instruments, applying the sends and panning them way the engineer does it. Generally, set everything up except the limiting and equalization processing. That's the engineer's territory.

If the engineer always uses certain setups, such as the high-hat all the way to the right, match his setup. Some engineers prefer to set the *record* levels so the multitrack returns come back to the console at 0VU, where all faders are at the same optimum level.

This is a good time for you to use your ears. Do some reasonable panning and sends to reverbs. Some engineers set the panning the way the players appear. For example, if a guitar player is always over to the right side, pan him to the right side in the monitor mix.

This is not the time to experiment with wild effects. Just do a basic mix. If the engineer hears that you can do good, quick, monitor mixes, he might in time let you spend more time behind the console—which is the goal.

CUE MIX

The monitor section is the channels returning from the multitrack. The cue mix is sent off the monitor section. When you are setting the cue mixes, wear the engineer's headphones and match the panning and levels to the engineer's monitor mix. For example, if the engineer has the rhythm guitar track all the way to the left, match it in the headphone cue mix. Keep the master headphone mix at a reasonable level, not so loud that it blasts the musician when he puts on the headphones. Better he ask for the headphone mix louder than quieter.

The importance of a good cue mix cannot be overstated. A musician recording with a good headphone cue mix can be the difference between an average performance, and an outstanding one.

RECORDING

Now everything is ready. The engineer has the right monitor mix, he is at the beginning of the song and track 13 is in *record-ready*. The microphones, limiting and equalization, and headphones are set and working normally, and the song cue numbers are in front of him.

Once the *record* button is pressed and the red record lights are on, write the new track information on the tracksheet, and document the setup. Watch that all the equipment is reacting properly and everything is going smoothly. Try not to leave the control room while any machine is in *record*.

PUNCHING IN AND OUT

As the tape-op, you will be punching in and out of record at exact spots during a song. If the producer tells you "punch in on the down beat of the third measure in the second chorus, and punch out at the end of the chorus," you must use the cues written down, your ears, your musical ability and your experience to punch in and out correctly. Remember these points:

- Do not press *record* if you are at all unsure of where the in and out points are. If you don't know, say that you want to hear the section once first to hear the correct spots. Punching in or out at the wrong spot may be disastrous, creating hours of extra work for everyone. It may also limit your chances of any engineering on the rest of the project.

- You can create a safety track by bouncing the section over to another track. Then if any important part on the master track is accidentally erased, a safety of the original is still intact. Digital safety tracks are routinely made, then bounced back into the master.

- Make sure the musician also knows the in and out punch points. Ask him to play along as soon as he hears the music, so the punch-in point is smoother.

- When repeatedly punching in the same part, go back to the same spot every time, about eight to ten seconds ahead of the punch-in point. This helps you count the correct amount of bars before punching in, and it also helps the musician know where he is within the song. Some multitrack machines automatically punch in and out at pre-determined points.

- Don't punch in or out on a sustaining note.

- Know the response time of the multitrack machine. Are the in and out punch points fast or slow? Check the crossfade times on digital machines, and adjust as necessary.

- After the take, go back and listen to the punch points. Sometimes a gulp sound is heard at the in or out point. If you accidentally record over something important, *you* will be making the gulp sound!

- Punches are meant to be clean and not heard. Sometimes the relays on the machines are heard just when the record button is pressed, but this hiccup is not recorded.

195

CHANGING TRACKS

With vocals, more than one track is almost always recorded. The singer might sing a song three or four times, just to get the feel of it. As each vocal pass is recorded on a different track, each track returns to a different channel on the console (with open reel machines, not always with DAWs).

For example, the engineer takes the previous track, 13, out of *record-ready* and switches the next one, 14, into *record-ready*. This means he wants to record another pass on track 14. Follow these steps:

1) Check that track 14 is open and available.

2) As the cue level and effects for the singer are sent to the headphones off of channel 13 on the console, match these settings on channel 14.

3) If the signal is being bussed, you may need to move the patchcord from the *record* input patch point of track 13, over to the *record* input patch point 14. During this change, the singer shouldn't hear any change in the headphones, or even be aware of any technicalities in the control room. Let her sing with no distractions. Depending on how the engineer has the microphone input channel set up, this step may not be needed.

4) Switch track 13 out of *record-ready* on the multitrack machine.

5) Press the cut button to mute track 13 from the room monitor and the headphones, including all effects.

6) Number each vocal pass on the tracksheet, and label each as a work track.

7) Another option is to patch the return of multitrack 14 into channel line input 13 so all the cue levels and sends stay the same. This works great until the musician wants to hear both tracks at the same time.

8) As the vocals are being recorded, write down the machine counter numbers on the lyric sheet for each line of the song. These line numbers are more detailed than the cue numbers written on the tracksheet, so any line in the song can be instantly found for a punch-in.

9) If the recording is on a DAW, the engineer may simply choose to record on other layers of track 13. DAW tracks have many layers for recording. Then he might *cut and paste* from the various layers to build one master vocal track.

BOUNCING AND COMPING

After any number of tracks are recorded, the engineer and producer might want to compile (or comp) the best parts of each track. They will listen to each track section by section, or line by line. The engineer will combine all these choice parts to one separate choice comp track.

COMPING TRACKS ON THE OPEN REEL

Commonly, the engineer chooses a source destination track, then sets the in and out points and establishes the crossfades. He then listens to the punches using the *rehearse* button to hear how they will sound. When he is happy, he takes the machine out of *rehearse* mode, and the punch is made. Or he may just punch in and out at the right spots, confident in his punching abilities and skill.

Once tracks have been bounced, erase, or clean the original tracks before re-recording. These tracks don't always have to be cleaned. With a digital open reel machine, any new program recorded on a track automatically erases the old program. But it is better to completely erase the old track and start fresh with a clean track, rather than chance hearing snippets of the old track come through, especially if there are a lot of punch-ins involved in the new track.

To clean tracks on a digital open reel machine, rewind the tape to the top of the song and put the appropriate track in *record-ready*. Activate the VSO, and raise the speed all the way up. Then press *record*. The track will erase, and it will take less time than letting the song play through at its normal speed. As the track is being erased, erase the track information on the tracksheet.

Listen to the song at a low volume as it plays at the increased speed, so you can press stop at the right time. You don't want to keep recording into the same track on the next song.

COMPING TRACKS ON THE DAW

Comping on a DAW is a one-person job, usually done by the engineer or a dedicated DAW operator working with the producer to choose the best bits. Everyone can see the vocal parts on the video screen, vastly aiding the editing process. After the vocal is comped—

• Listen through the song to confirm all crossfades are seamless.

• It may be your job to clean up the tracks. This does not mean going through and removing the naughty words, this means removing the obvious pops and buzzes. But wait—sounds such as breath on a vocal, or the occasional fret noise add to the character of a song. Avoid the *solo* button for this procedure. Most tracks that appear riddled with noises in *solo* are perfectly fine when the rest of the tracks are in the mix.

• Create a new layer, then copy and paste the new comp track.

• Label the new track, then consolidate. For example, a track labelled "Audio 10" results in the consolidated region with the same name. Maybe rename the comp track "Master Vocal" before consolidating.

• When consolidating, highlight all the comp tracks using the TOS and EOS markers, so all tracks start and end at the same spot.

VOCAL TUNING

An auto-tuner is a DAW plug-in, or a stand alone unit that tunes the vocal according to pre-determined settings. Before auto-tuning a vocal, make a copy of the track, then work on the copy. Some engineers tune the whole vocal track before mixing, while other engineers want to tune only the most obvious "off" bits, and leave the rest of the track untouched. Other engineers prefer to record until the vocalist sings everything properly, to avoid using an auto-tuner all together.

Once the main vocal track is recorded, edited and tuned, mark the appropriate spaces on the progress chart.

SLAVE SESSIONS

A slave of a song is a copy of the master tracks, mixed down to few guide tracks. This slave tape or file is used for additional recording, usually at other studios. If the master has, for example, nine tracks of drums, they might be submixed and bounced down to four or two tracks on the slave. All guitars and keyboards might be submixed and bounced to a pair of stereo tracks. This leaves many more tracks, or voices available for additional recording.

These guide tracks may be submixed and bounced again to a stereo mix on other tracks within the slave. One might think it is best to record a good stereo mix from all tracks on the master over to the slave, and simply use this mix for monitor during all the overdubs. However, keeping some instruments on separate tracks gives the engineer a degree of flexibility during overdubs and rough mixes.

OUTGOING

It is not uncommon for one song to be worked on in different studios, with different recording engineers, so there may be many slaves. If this is the case, the assistants are the ones who must keep all tracks organized.

- When the song file is going to another studio for additional work, confirm that the file contains all the correct tracks, with all the right parts, including a clearly labelled lead vocal. Sometimes a rough mix is printed to two separate tracks as a guide.

- Update the *session info* document file with house sync information, session dates and occurrences, plus any other relevant information. Include your name and contact information. Place this document in the *Master Session* file for clear and easy access. Commonly, there is one *session info* document per song. If necessary, include a *read me* file.

- Set your track count at less than 24, so a smaller receiving system can still open the file.

- If the outgoing slave is, for example, a guitar slave, place all the existing guitars on individual separate tracks, so the next engineer can *solo* them for the player to clearly hear what is there. He may not be able to make out exactly what is there if all the guitars are submixed together.

- Record the click track on a separate track.

- The frame rate on the slave must match the frame rate of the master.

- Keep the memory markers and tempo map.

- Record the effects plug-ins to a set of separate tracks. This avoids confusion if the other studio's DAW doesn't have the same plug-ins.

- As always, label DAW audio tracks before recording. This avoids having multiple files named 'Untitled 23465645'.

- Clearly label the session as a slave. This lets any user know that these tracks are not the original masters. In the old days of analog, better engineers could hear the difference between a master take and a second generation slave. With digital slaves this is not an issue.

- Include a Media Control Form (Figure 12.2) so the receiver has all the pertinent information.

- The master stays at your studio.

RETURNING DATA

When the slave data returns to your studio—

- Create a *Slave Session* folder for each returning slave.

- Return all the new tracks into the correct *Song Title—Master*, then import the compatible files into your *Master Session* file.

- Confirm that all tracks start at the proper time.

- Check for any notes or comments from the engineer who recorded the slave tracks, and bring them to the engineer's attention.

- Label which tracks are imported from the slave sessions, and which are from the original sessions.

- Verify the disc allocation settings for the incoming slave tracks.

- Don't import the bounced tracks that were made specifically for the slave. For example, if the drums were submixed and bounced to a stereo pair on the slave session, they will not be used on the final mix.

- Confirm which tracks are master tracks, and which are work tracks. Obviously the work tracks, or source tracks, are not meant to be used in the final mix. De-activate or mute them, then place these tracks at the bottom of the edit window, or hide them entirely.

- Confirm the session start time and frame rates are correct. Problems arise when a slave session is recorded on a newer or different program, or sample and bit rates do not match.

- Listen through to the end and confirm that the newly imported slave tracks correctly synchronize with the existing tracks. Listen for timing and tuning issues. Try panning an existing guitar track to the left, and an imported slave track to the right to confirm that the timing and tuning of the track matches the master tracks. As well, just looking at the new track may reveal whether it lines up correctly.

- Inform the engineer if you find any changes or edits that may affect the final outcome of the tracks.

- Don't hesitate to contact the assistant at the other studios if there are any questions or if any information is unclear.

. . . .

Summary

Chapter Ten explained what is expected of the assistant engineer while the overdubs are recorded:

- Changing reels and files to locate songs.

- Setting up the studio with a microphone, stand, and headphones.

- Setting up the console with new or previous sounds, and checking the signal flow for the overdub.

- Recording the overdub, bouncing, comping.

- Making slaves, importing and exporting session data.

CHAPTER ELEVEN

. . . .

Mixdown

At some point, every project is "mixed." Mixing is the process whereby all tracks, whether live or recorded, are combined, often with signal processing such as equalization, limiting, reverbs, and delays, typically to a pair of stereo tracks. Movie soundtracks may be mixed to three, four, five and even six tracks. All final mixes are then assembled and mastered. (See later in this chapter for mastering.) The final mastered product is then duplicated and distributed, but today's internet technology allows for alternate streams of distribution.

Mixing can take anywhere from a few moments, to a few hours to a few days. Big budget projects have been known to take weeks to mix one song, while jingles are commonly recorded and mixed in a single day.

Traditionally, songs have been mixed one at a time. The engineer would spend all day (or night) mixing and tweaking until everyone was happy. The client would take a copy of the mixes with him to listen to at home or in the car. The next day, the engineer would tweak any minor concerns, print the mix again, then move on. If the client chose to return to the mix again later, he could rest assured that the assistant had spent hours documenting each setting.

Today, the mixing starts well before the final tracks are completed. Automation, effects and processing can all be worked on, stored, then instantly retrieved allowing the engineer to fine tune the tracks as the recording process moves along. Big budget projects may hire a big gun mixer. Once he receives the tracks, he will of course start from scratch.

Sometimes after hearing the same song hundreds of times over, one loses a degree of perspective. On the first few times listening to a new song, there is a certain clarity of mind, where you can really hear what is needed. It is not uncommon to see mixers spend an hour two on one song, then move to another. Using a DAW, the mixer can open and close any mix at any time, and instantly pick up where he left off.

ROUGH MIXES

During a project, rough mixes, or roughs, are printed for everyone to take away from the studio and evaluate. They may be just a quick pass of the monitor mix, then printed on CD or loaded into an MP3 player. A full set of rough mixes might be made after basic tracks before all songs are completed, depending on how the engineer and producer prefer to work.

If you have the time, log all the roughs, because the heartbreak of ruff-itis may rear its ugly head. This is when someone keeps referring back to a rough mix for certain sounds or effects that he feels are needed on the final mix.

As with monitor mixes, if the engineer feels comfortable with the job you do, he may let you do the rough mixes. If he does, keep these mixes simple and basic. Use the same effects equipment and settings that the engineer uses. Do a basic rough mix, nothing radical, just so everything can be heard. This is not the time to do the world's most partyin' dance mix. You should know approximately how the engineer likes things panned, so be consistent with his preferences. Blend the most recent overdub with the rest of the tracks—don't make it the loudest thing in the mix.

FINAL MIXES

A mixdown session is essentially the same as a basics session, because many of the same rules apply. Throughout the session, you will be setting up outboard equipment, patching, changing and keeping track of all tapes, discs and recording media, helping the engineer at the console, and printing and logging the applicable information. The following are a few priorities for before, during, and after a final mix:

CONTROL ROOM

• Arrive well ahead of the session's scheduled start time so you can set everything up, arrange for any rental equipment, work on special alignments or equipment synchronization before the engineer arrives. The studio's technical department may need to be involved for some of the initial equipment setup.

• Clean and stock the control room. Bring enough supplies, including DVDs, DATs, CDs, Blu-Ray discs, data disks (if used), mixing tape (if used), labels and stationery, and leader tape. Choice takes will be head and tail leadered once the final analog mix is chosen.

• Again, to ensure safe passage throughout the halls of a busy recording studio, use a dedicated cart to bring supplies from the vault to the control room.

• If you are making more than one trip, bring up the mix machine alignment tape. Hopefully someone from the technical staff will begin the alignment while you, or better yet, a runner, schlep everything else into the control room.

- Find some extra empty reels (and boxes) for creating the master mix reels. When you need an empty reel and don't have one, splice off the remains of an almost empty reel with a razor blade, or spool the tape off the reel directly into the trash can. Check first that nothing important is being discarded.

- Bring all equipment scheduled for the mix, such as rental equipment, floaters, and the engineer's personal outboard rack into the room. Connect the appropriate equipment to the patchbay.

- Turn on, clean, and align all tape machines, and test all inputs and outputs. If necessary, load the computer with the data disk containing all of the song information. Enter any synchronizer offset, and confirm all machines are locking correctly.

- If necessary, load the multitrack machine with the appropriate tape, and wind it to the top of the song to be mixed. Return the head protector to its upright position.

- If applicable, open the song on the DAW, then place the curser at the top of the song.

CONSOLE

- Zero the console and add a fresh scribble strip. Don't write it out, as the engineer may want to change the layout of some tracks.

- Place the tracksheet and the cue sheet, if separate, on the console facing the engineer.

- Set up what you know the engineer will want for the mix, such as certain reverbs or delays on certain sends or busses. If you know he will want two channels for extra drum compression, go ahead and patch a stereo compressor into two channels. Patch out of an unused stereo buss, such as 15 or 16, into the input of a stereo compressor. Return the compressor into a stereo channel, or two properly panned mono channels. As a starting point for the engineer, set the compressor according to the setup sheet from a previous session. Set the buss output panning on all the drum channels to match the main monitor panning. This ensures that a drum that appears on the left side in the monitor, stays on the left side through the compressor. Confirm the setup works, properly label the channels, then lower the levels.

While setting up the session, check any notes from the recording sessions that the engineer may need for the mixing sessions, such as effects ideas or a alternate equalization.

DIGITAL AUDIO WORKSTATION

Open the *Song Title—Master* file and confirm that—

*   All tracks are visible, properly labelled, and correctly returning to the console, especially the correct lead vocal.

*   Imported tracks are correctly aligned with the existing tracks, and all tracks line up as they should.

*   Comments, notes or reminders in the comments section are noted.

*   Tracks not in use during the mix are removed or hidden.

*   Inputs, outputs, busses, inserts, outboard tracks, and all send inputs and outputs are clearly labelled in the I/O section.

*   Memory markers are correctly labelled for the changes throughout the song, from the first marker, labelled TOS to the last marker, labelled EOS.

- All pops and clicks at edit points have been eliminated.

- Any plug-in effects such as reverb and delay, are returning to their own separate tracks, not inserted into an audio track.

- Plug-ins on tracks that are not in use have been de-activated.

- A favorite rough mix has been lined up onto two tracks, so the engineer may use it as a reference.

Because plug-ins can bog down a system, have the engineer record a favorite plug-in sound to two tracks, then re-use the effect. As well, too much CPU activity may cause the automation to miss sections, or worse, cause a system error. If automation on a track is being used for a fade, it's better to remove the automation, copy the region to a new playlist as a safety, then apply auto-fade to the region. This results in a similar fade, without the use of automation.

ANALOG MIX MACHINE

By this point, the mixdown machines should be aligned and ready for use. Load the mixdown machine with a virgin mix tape, exercise it, and cue it up to the beginning of the tape. Then follow these steps:

- Switch the mixdown machines to *record-ready*. When any non-virgin tape other than the current mix tape is loaded on a mixdown machine, switch the machine out of *record-ready*.

- If mixes on your session are recorded directly to computer hard drive, set the input and output as you would a regular mixdown machine.
- Print a set of alignment tones to the mixdown machine as described in Chapter Four, and store these tones on Reel 1. Thirty seconds of each should be ample time.

- Don't leave the machine in *record-ready* if the tracks aren't intended for immediate recording. If the engineer looks over and sees a tape machine in *record-ready* and loaded with tape, he may accidentally record over yesterday's choice take. Any machine in *record-ready* is fair game.

DAT RECORDERS

DATs are popular because of the high quality reliable results, ease of use, compact size, and reasonable cost. Printing to DAT allows the mixer to choose a higher sampling rate than a standard CD. Better studios will stock the highest quality DAT tapes, because it does make a difference. Make note if external digital converters are used. Before printing mixes to DAT, print a set of tones as follows:

1) Exercise DAT cassettes the same as you would analog tapes. Load the tape, and fast-forward it all the way to the end, then rewind it back to the beginning. This allows the tape to align to the machine's torquing.

2) Put the DAT machine in *record-ready*, then disengage the automatic indexing function. The automatic indexing function assigns one ID number to each musical passage. When the engineer presses "3" on the DAT machine, he should hear the third pass, not the third tone.

3) Set the console oscillator output to 0VU on the master meters, as described in Chapter Four.

4) Set the input meters on the DAT machine to your studio standard. Different studios may vary between a standard input level of somewhere between -12dB to -20dB = 0VU. This allows 12 to 20dB of headroom before clipping. One clipped level can ruin an entire pass.

5) Reading A-time, or absolute (real) time on the DAT machine, record 15 seconds of blank tape, then record a 1kHz tone.

6) At 45 seconds, change the tone to 10kHz.

7) At 1 minute 15 seconds, change the tone to 50Hz.

8) At 1 minute 45 seconds, mute the input of the DAT machine and let the tape roll past the 2 minute mark, then stop the machine.

9) Restart the automatic indexing feature so the first mix printed to tape is indexed as "1."

10) DAT machines can show the input levels without being in *record-ready* mode. Don't leave the machine in *record-ready* or it might automatically go into *record* after a few minutes. The DAT machine is now ready.

CD BURNERS

Most studios have at least one permanently mounted CD burner normalled to the output of the console. When several copies must be made, additional burners have to be brought in, or many passes must be made to the limited number of available machines.

If the input is digital, the *record* level will not be adjustable. Simply switch the input button to "digital." If the input to the burner is analog, adjust the input levels so the signal is loud enough, but not overloading. The input will be from one of two sources: either from a master mixdown machine, or live from the console's main buss output.

AS THE MIX BEGINS

As the mix begins, make sure the engineer is comfortable. Give him the best chair, maybe pour him a cup of coffee or bring him a soda, and assure him that all equipment is set up and properly connected—and maybe lower the lights a bit.

PATCHING

Create an updated list describing all patches, including crosspatches, inserts, busses, sends and returns, and include all outboard equipment being used. Whenever a patch is added, changed, or revised, note the change on the list. Leave the patch list on the console where the engineer can see it and understand it at a glance. After the mix, use the list to check off each patch as you remove it to confirm that all patches are correctly logged.

CROSSPATCHING

The layout of tracks on the tracksheet is not always how the engineer wants them to appear at the console while mixing. Crosspatching allows the routing of a track return normally returning to one channel line input, over to another. Tracks are crosspatched to different channels for many different reasons.

- To split tracks containing more than one instrument for individual processing. For example, Figure 11.3 shows track 15 contains two different instruments in two different sections of the song, so it is patched into channels 16 and 27. Each channel is processed separately, with one muted while the other plays.

- To group, or re-arrange the returns for familiarity. For example, the engineer may always prefer the lead vocal track to return in channel 24.

- To arrange tracks from the slave machine so they return with the rest of the instruments. For example, if the choice background vocal tracks on the slave tape are on tracks 8 and 9, these might be patched over to where the other vocals are returning on the console.

- Some consoles have certain channels that house better equalization modules than the rest of the channels on the console. The engineer may want specific tracks, such as vocals, in these channels because of their superior sound qualities. Of course, digital tracks are all the same, and are easily moved as well, so this isn't an issue.

ADDITIONAL PATCHING

- When crosspatching, check that all the tracks are patched into the console. A small part recorded late at night, or early in the project could be overlooked, so put a check mark on each track on the tracksheet as each patch is made. The tracksheet will be covered with check marks, but so what? After the mix, the tracksheet will probably no longer be needed.

- After patching a piece of outboard equipment, label the unit with a small strip of adhesive tape, stating the send into it and where it returns on the console. The engineer wants to see, with a quick look around the control room, what each piece of equipment is being used for. You might even want to label his beverage. All too often I've heard someone in a session ask, "Is this your soda or mine?"

- Use the enclosed delay chart, Figure 11.1, to write the exact ¼, ⅓, and ½ note delay times from the BPM as written on the tracksheet, and in the DAW's *session info* window. The engineer will use these numbers to set his delay and echo pre-delay times of the song.

  A quarter note delay in milliseconds, or ms. is determined by dividing 60,000 (number of ms. in one minute) by the BPM of the song. Once this is established, other delays times are determined by multiplication, such as multiplying by 1.5 for the dotted third, or by .666 for triplets.

- As the session begins, listen to the song and time exactly 10 seconds, then multiply the beats by 6. For example, 15 beats in a 10 second period, multiplied by 6 is 120 BPM. According to Figure 11.1, the ¼ note for 120 BPM is 500ms. Set this delay as a starting point for the engineer.

- Many pieces of outboard equipment have internal storage capacity. Once the engineer sets the parameters, write them down on the setup sheet, then store them internally. If the unit is accidentally unplugged, or if a future re-mix is imminent, the settings are easily retrievable.

BPM	1/4	1/4 triplet	1/8	1/8 triplet	1/16	1/16 triplet
80	750.00	500.25	375.00	250.12	187.50	125.06
81	740.74	494.07	370.37	247.04	185.19	123.52
82	731.71	488.05	365.85	244.02	182.93	122.01
83	722.89	482.17	361.45	241.08	180.72	120.54
84	714.29	476.43	357.14	238.21	178.57	119.11
85	705.88	470.82	352.94	235.41	176.71	17.71
86	697.67	465.35	348.84	232.67	174.63	116.34
87	689.66	460.00	344.83	230.00	172.62	115.00
88	681.82	454.77	340.91	227.39	170.68	113.69
89	674.16	449.66	337.08	224.83	168.81	112.42
90	666.67	444.67	333.33	222.33	166.00	111.17
91	659.34	439.78	329.67	219.89	164.25	109.95
92	652.17	435.00	326.09	217.50	163.57	108.75
93	645.16	430.32	322.58	215.16	161.94	107.58
94	638.30	425.74	319.15	212.87	159.36	106.44
95	631.58	421.26	315.79	210.63	157.84	105.32
96	625.00	416.88	312.50	208.44	156.38	104.22
97	618.56	412.58	309.28	206.29	154.96	103.14
98	612.24	408.37	306.12	204.18	153.59	102.09
99	606.06	404.24	303.03	202.12	151.27	101.06
100	600.00	400.20	300.00	200.10	150.00	100.05
101	594.06	396.24	297.03	198.12	148.77	99.06
102	588.24	392.35	294.12	196.18	147.59	98.09
103	582.52	388.54	291.26	194.27	145.45	97.14
104	576.92	384.81	288.46	192.40	144.35	96.20
105	571.43	381.14	285.71	190.57	143.29	95.29
106	566.04	377.55	283.02	188.77	141.26	94.39
107	560.75	374.02	280.37	187.01	140.28	93.50
108	555.56	370.56	277.78	185.28	139.33	92.64
109	550.46	367.16	275.23	183.58	137.42	91.79
110	545.45	363.82	272.73	181.91	136.55	90.95
111	540.54	360.54	270.27	180.27	135.70	90.14
112	535.71	357.32	267.86	178.66	133.89	89.33
113	530.97	354.16	265.49	177.08	132.12	88.54
114	526.32	351.05	263.16	175.53	131.37	87.76
115	521.74	348.00	260.87	174.00	130.65	87.00
116	517.24	345.00	258.62	172.50	129.97	86.25
117	512.82	342.05	256.41	171.03	128.31	85.51
118	508.47	339.15	254.24	169.58	127.68	84.79
119	504.20	336.30	252.10	168.05	126.08	84.08
120	500.00	333.50	250.00	166.75	125.00	83.38
121	495.87	330.74	247.93	165.37	123.97	82.69
122	491.80	328.03	245.90	164.02	122.95	82.01
123	487.80	325.37	243.90	162.68	121.95	81.34
124	483.87	322.74	241.94	161.37	120.97	80.69
125	480.00	320.16	240.00	160.08	120.00	80.04
126	476.19	317.62	238.01	158.81	119.05	79.40
127	472.44	315.12	236.22	157.56	118.11	78.78
128	468.75	312.66	234.38	156.33	117.19	78.16
129	465.12	310.23	232.56	155.12	116.28	77.56
130	461.54	307.85	230.77	153.92	115.38	76.96

Figure 11.1 Delay Chart

Also, if the engineer is limited in outboard equipment, he may need different settings for different parts of a song. For example, you may need to change the settings on a digital reverb for the choruses, then go back to the original setting for the rest of the song. With each setting stored internally, the programs can be changed with the press of one button. Of course, this change is needed every time a mix is printed.

DURING THE MIX

During the mix—

- Watch that all the equipment is acting and reacting how the engineer wants it—not necessarily correctly, but how he wants it. For example, some engineers like to record to analog with very hot levels. If the input meters on the mix machines look too high or low, bring it to his attention before the printing begins.

- Listen for stray sounds, or for tracks that are on but should be off, or tracks that are off that should be on.

- If the session requires you to connect and disconnect cables at the back of any machines, label them with a piece if adhesive tape, stating the original routing. If these changes need to stay for the next session, leave a note for the next assistant explaining exactly what was changed, and why.

- Keep smiling. Mixing can be draining for everyone in the room, including you. A good attitude throughout the session will keep things rolling a whole lot easier.

PRINTING THE MIX

The four methods in use for printing a mix today are—

- A to A (analog to analog). The songs are played from an analog recorder through an analog console, then recorded onto analog tape, either $^{1}/_{4}$" or $^{1}/_{2}$". This has been the traditional method of mixing since Elvis.

- A to D. The analog signal is routed through digital converters, then recorded to a digital source, such as a DAT or CD.

- D to A. The digital signal is converted to analog, then recorded onto analog tape.

214

- D to D. The signal remains within the digital realm, and either the song is stored as a file, or the mixer connects to an external machine, such as DAT via digital cables.

INPUT LEVELS

Whatever format your session mixes to—

- If the signal originates from a master mixdown machine, check that left stays left and right stays right.

- Set the levels while the engineer is doing the mix. Don't wait until he is ready to press *record* to check the input level to the machines. When he is ready, the mix machines should be too.

- When setting levels, use the loudest section from the source. Peak levels should come close to the red on the VU meter. The ideal level is hot, but not so hot that it distorts the signal.

- The engineer may mix a song louder on one day than on the previous day, so make sure all the *record* levels are consistent.

- Watch the input levels during recording. If any levels seem unusual during the pass, again, note the counter numbers. After the pass, rewind to the loudest section and, using headphones, listen for distortion.

OPEN REEL

If your session is printing to analog tape—

- Check the record alignment of each virgin mix reel as it is loaded.

- While printing the mix, use the input/output button on the mixdown machine to compare the input levels with the output levels. If the input levels are different than the output levels, the alignment may be off.

- Confirm the tape is parked correctly before pressing *record*. Nothing important should get lost.

- Clean the heads on the *slap* machine before recording the mix, and make sure there is enough tape on the supply reel to last throughout the song. Tape slap is an older method of delay using a mixdown machine with a varispeed. Due to the abundance of digital delays available, this archaic method of delay is used today for a specific sound.

- Note the slate number and machine counter number for each mix on a takesheet.

- As printing to the mix machine begins, note where on the tape the slate is, and where the song starts. If you need to stop and rewind to record over the last pass, keep the original slate and tell the engineer. Most machines have a RTZ (return to zero) button, or number storage function that can be used when shuttling the tapes. When the RTZ button is pressed, the tape machine rewinds to zero on the tape counter. Don't record over previous passes unless the producer or engineer specifically tells you to.

- Even with computer mixdown automation, manual moves on the console are still common. For example, a send needs to be turned up for one snare hit. Put a tiny piece of red adhesive tape on the specific send on the snare channel, so the engineer knows at a glance which knob to turn up.

- Don't press the *stop* button until the engineer tells you. If the ending of a song is cut off, such as the ending of a fade, too much time may be wasted editing on a new fade.

- Define the differences between mixes clearly. Often, without talking to you, the producer and engineer will discuss running a pass with, for instance, more bass guitar. Write this on a takesheet or tape label with any other differences between mixes.

- Completely log and organize all mixes, incomplete mixes, outtakes and everything else recorded. You need to know exactly where everything is when the editing and assembly begins.

- Never let the tape run out while recording. If you aren't sure that there is enough room left on the tape for a complete take, change tapes before starting another take. Everyone will understand having to wait an extra minute or two while you change tapes. They won't understand losing the end of a fantastic take because the tape ran out.

- When the analog reel is not in motion, place sticky round dots (available at any stationery store) or a small piece of splicing tape on the analog tape to mark the takes. This is a fast and efficient method, used when the machine is in rewind, to pinpoint precise locations as each flag goes by. However, some engineers may not want the mix tapes peppered with sticky dots.

DIGITAL AUDIO TAPE CASSETTE MACHINE

If your session is printing to DAT—

- Set the input levels as close to zero as possible without overload. Once that level is established, lower the input by 4 to 6dB. Unlike analog recording, lower levels are not lower quality—to a point. Just the opposite, lower input levels can capture peaks cleaner. This only applies within a defined level, where the signal is properly recorded.

- As you record a pass to DAT, use a takesheet to note the program ID numbers, the absolute time, the take number and any relevant notes, such as "louder vocal" or "needs edit in second chorus". A DAT can hold a lot of information, so rather than writing all the takes on that little card that comes with the DAT, write everything on a takesheet, then neatly transfer the information to the card at a more convenient time.

- Before removing any DAT tape from the machine, rewind the tape to the beginning. This minimizes the possibility of the machine's mechanisms eating the tape in the middle of anything important.

- If applicable, check that the DAT is parked at the correct spot. Many mistakes in the studio can be repaired, but once something is erased, it's gone.

CD BURNER

If your session is printing to a CD burner—

- Determine the normal. If the signal originates from the console's main buss output, the input to the CD burner is probably normalled from the console.

- Make the patch. If the signal originates from the console's main buss output, and the CD burners are patched from a master mixdown machine, their normal input from the console is defeated. To regain the normal, don't pull all the input patches from each CD burner. At the patchbay, pull the output patches from the master mixdown machine, and patch them to the main output from the console. This will send the main console output buss to the inputs of the CD burners.

- Check the CD in a stand alone CD player after the burn. Some discs won't play on all CD players. It's important for the producer to hear these mixes in the car on the way to the next party.

DISC/DAT LABELLING

When labelling the various discs and DATs, use proper studio labels. Write the necessary information on the label as neatly as possible, including:

- The name of the artist and the contents, such as *rough mixes*. Discs and DATs containing the final assembled mixes should have neat and clear labels. These copies of the final masters should look as professional as possible.

- The name of each song, its indexing or location on the disc, the date, and maybe note the last overdub recorded so the listener knows how current the mix is. If anyone needs more information on a specific mix or version of a song, look at the date on the label, and refer to your daily log for complete details.

- The name of the person who gets the CD. For example, when the session is over and everyone wants a copy of the mixes in a different order.

Once everything needed is on the CD, check if the client wants anything else included. Then burn the CDs. If the artist gives you a CD he wants to use as a reference, return it to the proper owner by the end of the session.

EDITING THE MIX

Every edit piece removed from the master mixes must be labeled and stored for easy retrieval. There may eventually be many mixes of a song, such as the single mix, the album mix, the extended mix, the 12" mix, the dance mix, and so on. For a jingle, many different versions may also be needed, such as long versions, short versions, versions with backing vocals, without backing vocals, donuts and more.

All must be labeled and organized so that any mix can be easily found. Time schedules on jingles do not allow for extra time to hunt around looking for lost pieces of music.

TAPE EDITS

This section on edits is primarily for open reel recording. Before the engineer splices the final mix tape, he might try a trial edit. After confirming that the edits will work, he then splices the mix tape. (The difference between a splice and an edit is, the tape is spliced, the music is edited.) Tape is traditionally spliced using a razor blade and splicing tape.

Of course, digital editing on the DAW is now more common that analog editing. When a shorter mix is needed, the engineer will make a copy of the *Master Mix*, then digitally edit it rather than resort to the razor blade.

Some engineers still prefer mixing to, and editing on, analog tape. Be prepared to help with the following:

• Confirm that the machines are well lit, cleaned, demagnetized and correctly wired.

• Have on hand fresh sharp razor blades—lots of them. The engineer may discard them after one or two splices. Demagnetize them so there is no chance of signal erasure where the razor contacts the tape. Open the cardboard sleeve holding the razor, but leave the razor within the sleeve. This way the engineer knows the razor is unused, yet easy for him to retrieve.

• When discarding used blades, don't just toss them into the trash. Either put them in a small used razor box or tape the razor's edge with adhesive tape before throwing it away, so whoever changes the trash bags won't accidentally get sliced. I accidentally cut my finger open during the recording of KISS's "Animalize" and spilled blood all over the machine. Gene Simmons praised me for "getting into the vibe."

- Sharpened white grease pencils. The engineer needs to mark the exact spot on the tape using a grease pencil with a nice sharp point. Rub the grease pencil, or china marker on a piece of scrap paper while spinning it on the paper, giving the pencil a good sharp point, then cut off the excess string. Simple, yes—but it can be the attention to detail that makes clients and engineers want to work with you in the future.

- Leader tape. Ask the engineer if he wants paper or plastic leader, and what width and color of splicing tape he prefers.

- An edit reel. This reel holds the sections removed from the choice takes. Use a takesheet to mark all the edit pieces clearly, and to organize them by the song, section of the song, length of the section removed, the take, and the date. Leader edited sections by song, and write each song title on the leader tape. As well, write the titles on the reel, as in Figure 8.5. The edits must be organized in case the producer wants an edit returned back into a song.

- A clean splicing block. Before use, clean the splicing block with cotton and alcohol to remove any studio grime and grunge, then demagnetize the block. Some engineers prefer the kind of splicing block with the arms that flip down to hold the tape in the block. Some prefer the kind where the tape fits in snugly without any arms holding it in place. Splicing blocks are made to fit two layers of tape. Both layers are cut, spliced together, and the excess sections of tape are removed.

  Some engineers use different splicing angles for different sorts of edits. One angle might be used if the edits are between songs, and another angle might be used if the edits are within a song. Other engineers find an angle on the splicing block that they like and use it for all edits. If you are helping with the splicing, use the angle he uses.

- Clean hands. The oils on your fingers transfer onto tape, so clean hands are essential.

- Your full attention. The engineer needs your attention, because if he needs a section of a song from another reel, or from somewhere else, you must be on full alert so he can concentrate on the editing process, not hunting around for an elusive piece of music.

DURING THE EDITS

When the engineer is editing, he is counting on you to help keep everything organized. You must—

- Stay at the console. He may want you at the console to raise or lower the monitor level.

- Keep up. As he is *scrubbing* the tape, manually moving it back and forth over the heads to find the exact edit point, make sure he knows which playback head he is monitoring and that he is at the right spot before the edit, and not, for example, on the wrong chorus.

- Use an additional machine. Many control rooms have access to more than one mixdown machine. If possible, use another machine for organizing the various sections of tape while the engineer edits on the main machine. If he needs a piece of tape from another reel, you can quickly find it using the second machine. This second machine can also be used throughout the session for organizing master reels, locating sections, editing, and leadering while the main machine is in use.

- Be quiet. Wait for the right moment to ask non-essential questions. Asking him what he thought of last night's hockey game during an important edit may not be appropriate. Let him concentrate.

- Stay organized. In the daily log, keep track of the origin of every piece from a choice take. If any additional editing is needed, or if an edit needs to be returned to the mix, the complete layout of where all the sections originated is available.

UNDOING A TAPE EDIT

Sometimes, edits need replacing, which means the splice must be opened, and the original section of the song returned. With clean hands, use your fingers to carefully remove the piece of splicing tape. If this doesn't work, try careful use of a razor blade. If any glue from the splicing tape stays on the back of the audio tape, wrap up a ball of splicing tape with the sticky side out and pat the area to remove the excess glue. Find the right section of tape to be returned using the information in the daily log.

PRACTICE YOUR EDITS

In off time, practice your editing skills. Maybe the engineer on your project will let you practice editing the outtakes. If not, use a house mix tape after asking for permission, of course. House tapes are used by the technical staff to test equipment and do alignments, and by assistants for practice.

At one end of the reel, not in the middle, record a song or section of a song from a CD. Practice your editing skills by moving the verses around, or extending the ending. This is good practice for when you're called upon to do the leadering and assembly of master reels.

COPIES

Throughout the project, the people in the session may want to take copies of the day's work home. The engineer rough mixes the song, then you make the copies. Each person involved usually receives a copy, except you. Making copies of the day's work is an important aspect of your job. You have to make the copies, clearly label every mix printed, along with the date and the artist.

Sometimes, at the end of a long session, when all that's left is a quick cleanup then home to bed, the producer mentions he needs 10 copies, each with the songs in a different order—and he needs them first thing tomorrow morning. Your first thought is to pummel him with the closest dull object, but you realize the closest dull object is the bass player.

THE COPY ROOM

Most larger studios have a designated room where all the copies are made because using the control room ties up valuable studio time. If the studio records jingles, a copy room is necessary because many copies of different formats and lengths are needed daily. The size of a copy room can vary from a small room with only two machines, to a large fully staffed room with banks of machines for mass duplication.

Because many different formats come through the studio, the copy room should have the proper machines to fit any need, including digital and analog formats. Of course, making copies within a program on the host computer is quick and relatively easy, but it is often necessary to make copies using external CD burners.

- When additional burners are brought in for multiple copies, they are connected via the patchbay. Consult with the technical department before plugging the balanced XLR mix buss at the console into the burners unbalanced RCA inputs.

- At the patchbay, use a mult to split the signal output from one mixdown machine into the inputs of the CD burners, so many copies can be made at once.

- Digital signals cannot be multed. Commonly, one cable connects the host computer to the burner.

- Due to studio grounding issues, don't make copies when a master mix is being printed. Signal from the copies can leak into the main studio monitor buss, and may inadvertently print onto the master mix.

- Leave as little room as possible between songs. Even a few seconds is too long.

Every copy leaving the studio must be properly labeled and checked for accuracy before going out.

YOUR PERSONAL COLLECTION

Recording copies of any sessions to take them home for your listening pleasure is illegal. Those songs don't belong to you, the studio, the producer, or the engineer—they belong to the band, the record company, the ad agency, or the financial backer. If it falls into the wrong hands, such as a radio station, it will be traced to your studio, and finally to you. No one will want to work with you if they think that their rough mixes will land on the streets. No band wants their project heard outside the studio until it's been completed. They want the listener to enjoy the music to its fullest, not half finished. Plus it's a respect thing.

AFTER THE MIX

DOCUMENTING THE MIX

Once the mix is done, the session must be documented. A mix is logged so that all the mix settings can be returned to at any time in the future. Songs may be re-mixed for a variety of reasons. Perhaps the original mix is unsatisfactory, and needs more work. Settings on all equipment used are reset exactly, and the engineer either repairs the questionable parts and re-prints the mix, or he continues mixing the song until everyone is satisfied. Setup sheets help log the mix correctly.

MIX SETUP SHEETS

Final mixes on large projects will always need to be logged. Setup sheets that are used to write down the mixes tend to be more in-depth than setup sheets used to write down individual sounds due to the amount of equipment involved. Every channel, patch, and setting must be logged precisely and clearly. One small error may mean a significant change in the sound of the mix.

If the engineer is mixing one song per session, the mix can usually be logged after the session ends. However, if more than one song is being mixed in a single session, begin the logging well before the mix is ready to be printed. The session shouldn't have to wait while you log the mix.

Start logging the mix about halfway through the session, when the actual sounds are probably set, and the engineer is concentrating on the individual channel mutes, pans and levels. Some mixes, such as jingles, are rarely logged, due to lack of time. Most studios have a standard in place that all the assistants follow. The setup sheet is broken down into three basic sections: session information, patching, and outboard equipment.

SESSION INFORMATION

The session information in Figure 11.2 includes—

• The date, artist, producer, engineer, assistant, and specific studio within the premises—such as studio A or B, client, tape speed, varispeed, offsets between machines, master or slave information, alignment and timecode information, and formats. Digital information such as bit depth and sampling rate would go here as well.

226

- The name and number of the song and specific mix logged. If there are 10 mixes of a certain song, settings of equipment may change slightly between the printing of mix 1 and mix 10. Each change needs to be logged.

- Any section of the console not retained in the computer, such as the master send and return levels, console compression and maybe subgroups.

- The specific mixdown machines used. Larger studios may have many machines, all used in different sessions and situations. Different machines, even the same make and model, may have slight variations in sound reproduction.

With computer recall, the logging of the console settings is as easy as pressing a key on the computer to store the settings. However, this system is accurate only to a point. The engineer understands this, and will use the setup as a starting point for the re-mix.

When songs are mixed to both tape and DAW, titles and numbers should correspond to the tape labels and setup sheets. All mixes must be numbered on the DAW with cross references to the setup sheets.

PATCHING

All patches, including their origin and destination, must be logged.

- Crosspatches. Write the track number from the master or slave, its input to the console, and the name of the track as it appears on the strip. Compare the layout of the instruments on the tracksheet (Figure 8.2) to the layout of the tracks on the console during mixdown (Figure 11.3). This is how the instrument layout of the console appears for the mix.

- Sends and effects returns. These are noted on both the setup sheet, and on the equipment's faceplate (Figure 11.4). For example, notice that sends 5 and 6 are sent into digital reverb 1 then return into channel line inputs 33 and 34. The setup sheet shows where the sends originated, and where the unit is returning.

- Individual channel inserts, along with the equipment patched into each point. For example, in channel 2 the signal flows out of the insert point, into a limiter, into an equalizer, and then back into the insert return.

- Bussing, or group outputs. During mixing, busses might be used to send signal from individual channels to outboard effects. For example, buss 1 on channel 3 is pressed. Channel 3, the kick drum, is being sent to an effect, then returns to line input 4. Channel 3 is the only channel on the console with buss 1 pressed, as the kick drum track should be the only channel into the effect.

OUTBOARD EQUIPMENT

Log the settings of each piece of outboard equipment by using a copy of the faceplate (Figure 11.5). As mentioned in Chapter Nine, most equipment manuals come with a template of the unit's faceplate. Photocopy this template and use it to write down the settings of the unit. Studios may have faceplate sheets available, and sometimes the faceplates are stored in a computer file, then printed as needed. Included in this section of the setup sheet is—

- Everything about the actual unit, including the faceplate, the inputs and outputs, all the internal settings, any controls on the rear of the unit, and include outboard equipment patched in but deactivated.

- The specific piece of outboard equipment used in the mixdown, plus its send, return or insert point used, as a cross reference with the patching section.

An equalizer or limiter with only a few dials can be simply marked down, such as "Input 7.2, Output 5.5," with no need for an illustration. Yet again, whatever system is in use at your studio is the correct system to use.

Artist _Tuff Beans_____ Project# _631_____
Song _Wiener Water Soup Blues - Mix 6_____ Date _December 06, Year_
Label_ Crapitol Records_ Contact _____ Phone ( ) _____
Producer _Bob Loblaw_____ Phone ( ) _____
Engineer _Casey Jones_____ Phone ( ) _____
Assistant Engineer _A. Reader_____ Phone ( ) _____

ANALOG MACHINE INFORMATION

Analog Tape Machine(s) _A-80__ Tracks _1/2" 2 track___ Tape Speed _30 ips___
Tones _Reel 1_____ Ref. Level 0VU = _370 nwm_ Noise Reduction _None_____

Time Code Format	☐ 30	☐ 29.97 NDF	☐ 24	☐ SMPTE	Sync Ref (For master)
				☐ EBU	
	☐ 25	☐ 29.97 DF		☐ MTC	

DIGITAL MACHINE INFORMATION

Digital Machine _DAT #2__ Tracks _____ Tape Speed _____

| Bit Depth | ☐ 16 | Sample Rate | ☐ 44.1 ☐ 88.2 ☐ 192 |
| | ☒ 24 Other _____ | | ☒ 48 ☐ 96 ☐ Other_____ |

Time Code Format	☐ 30	☐ 29.97 NDF	☐ 24	☐ SMPTE	Sync Ref (For master)
				☐ EBU	
	☐ 25	☐ 29.97 DF		☐ MTC	

DAW INFORMATION

DAW Platform ☒ Mac ☐ PC ☐ Other DAW Program _Pro tools_____
Host Computer _Mac Jupiter_ Host Computer OS _OX12.5_ Software Version _23.5_____

| Bit Depth | ☐ 16 | Sample Rate | ☐ 44.1 ☐ 88.2 ☐ 192 |
| | ☒ 24 Other _____ | | ☒ 48 ☐ 96 ☐ Other_____ |

Time Code Format	☒ 30	☐ 29.97 NDF	☐ 24	☒ SMPTE	Sync Ref (For master)
				☐ EBU	
	☐ 25	☐ 29.97 DF		☐ MTC	

File Format ☐ BWAV ☐ AIFF ☒ WAV ☐ MP3 ☐ OTHER _____
Sync Source _____ Hard Disc _____ Notes _____
Plug ins _____

SSL Plug-ins

Neve 4020 plug-ins V7.3.2

Figure 11.2 *Session Information*

LINE IN	PROGRAM	SOURCE TRACK	TAPE MON IN	LINE IN	PROGRAM	SOURCE TRACK	TAPE MON IN
1	Bass amp	2		33			
2	Bass direct	3		34			
3	Kick drum	4		35			
4	Kick sample	buss 3		36			
5	Snare drum	5		37			
6	Snare sample	buss 4		38			
7	High hat	6		39			
8	Toms left	7		40			
9	Toms right	8		41			
10	Cymbals left	9		42			
11	Cymbals right	10		43			
12	Ambiance left	11		44			
13	Ambience right	12		45			
14	Horns left	slave 15		46			
15	Horns right	slave 16		47			
16	Guitar 1	15		48			
17	Guitar 1 double	17		49			
18	Guitar 2	16		50			
19	Acoustic gtr 1	17		51			
20	Acoustic gtr 2	22		52			
21				53			
22	Backgr. vocals 1	slave 9		54			
23	Backgr. vocals 2	slave 10		55			
24	Lead vocal	18		56			
25	Keyboards left	19		57			
26	Keyboards right	20		58			
27	Tambourine	15		59			
28				60			
29	Flanger left	buss 1		61			
30	Flanger r			62			
31	Delay 1	buss 6		63			
32	Delay 2	buss 7		64			

Figure 11.3 *Patching*

SEND	EFFECT	RETURN
1	Delay 3 ---> Echo Chamber 1	Stereo Return # 1
2	Delay 4 ---> Echo Chamber 2	Stereo Return # 2
3	Harmonizer #1	Stereo Return # 3
4		
5		
STEREO L	Stereo Delay L	Stereo return # 4 L
STEREO R	Stereo Delay R	Stereo return # 4 R

INSERT OUT	INSERTS	INSERT IN
2	Limiter # 1 ---> Equalizer # 1	2
3	Limiter # 2 ---> Equalizer # 2	3
4	Equalizer # 3	4
6	Equalizer # 4	6
12	Noise Gate # 1	12
13	Noise Gate # 2	13
16	Limiter # 3	16
24	De-esser ---> Limiter # 4	24

BUSS	EFFECT	RETURN
1	Flanger	Line inputs 29, 30
3	Noise gate ---> Kick Sample	Line input 4
4	Noise gate ---> Snare Sample	Line input 6
6	Digital Delay # 1	Line input 31
7	Digital Delay # 2	Line input 32
12	Trigger to noise gate 1	
13	Trigger to noise gate 2	

Figure 11.4 *Sends and Returns*

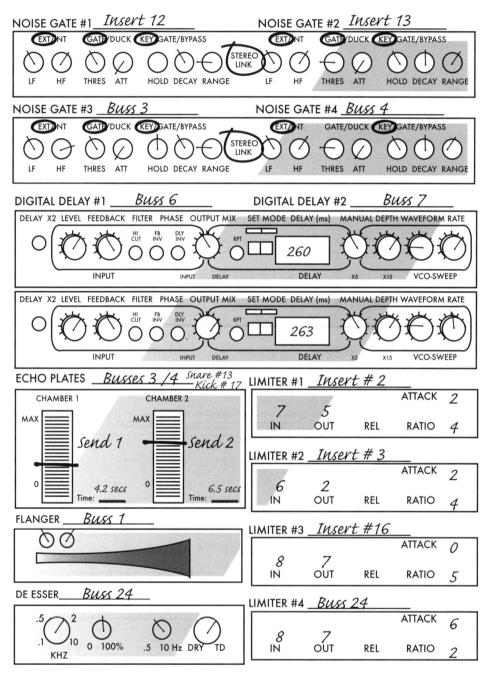

Figure 11.5 *Outboard Equipment*

If you have free access to a photocopy machine, you might create one master mix sheet, and simply re-use it. When the settings for the mix are correctly written down (in pencil), photocopy the complete setup sheet, making sure everything is legible. This copy is kept and used for the re-mix. Erase all the settings on the master sheet, and re-use it, updating it with the new title and mix information. As engineers tend to be fairly consistent throughout the mixing of a project, some patches and settings might stay the same for every mix.

SETUP SHEET STORAGE

Once the mixes are logged, the setup sheets are stored in a safe place in case of a re-mix. Mix setup sheets can be quite bulky. You might need to keep them in a large manila envelope with everything else.

BREAKING DOWN THE MIX

Once the mix is completely logged, zero the console, patchbay, and outboard equipment. But before you start pulling patches—for your own benefit—take a moment to see and hear what the engineer did. *Solo* a track, then press the bypass buttons and listen to the differences in sound. If he is, for example, running a vocal through a limiter, then a compressor, then an equalizer, then a de-esser, determine why he is doing that and why in that specific order.

If you examine the equalization settings on other tracks, such as guitars, you will see that the engineer is probably pulling equalization on the other tracks where he is adding equalization on the vocal. If he is adding 100Hz on the bass guitar track, he would most likely lower 100Hz on the rhythm guitar. Good engineers use equalization to establish distinction in each in-strument. In a good mix, every instrument occupies its own space.

- Start the mix breakdown at the patchbay, not at the console. If any odd or unusual routing appears while breaking down the bay, the signal flow can still be traced at the console.

233

- Remove each patchcord individually. Don't grab a handful of patches and yank, which is always a temptation. Use the engineer's patch list to check off each patchcord pulled, and see that the equipment settings on each unit are correctly logged. When all patches are pulled from the bay, and all changes on the setup sheet are checked, the sheet must be correct.

- Finally, if adhesive tape was used on the scribble strip, save it by rolling it up like a regular roll of tape. Pull down all faders, zero the console, and clean up as you would after any session.

SETTING UP A RE-MIX

Setting up a re-mix should take no more than an hour, depending on how complicated the original mix was:

1) Bring all the outboard equipment used in the original mix into the control room. Plug everything in, then turn on all the equipment.

2) Label the console with the adhesive strip used on the original mix. If it isn't available, re-label the strip on the console using the setup sheet.

3) If a computer recall was used, find the corresponding setup and reset the console. If no computer was used, you must reset every single knob.

4) Load the proper tape and wind it to the top of the song.

5) Once the console is properly set, make the crosspatches according to Figure 11.3. When the crosspatches are complete, check that all tracks returning to the console correspond to the strip on the console.

6) Patch in the outboard equipment and label each unit, as was done for the original. Match the outboard equipment with the settings written down, front and back.

7) Set the master send and return levels.

234

8) Play the song again and check all outboard equipment for proper input level, signal flow, internal settings, master levels, and returns.

9) Load the original mix on the mixdown machine. Play the original mix and your re-mix off the console, starting both versions at exactly the same time, so that you hear song continuity as you switch between the original mix and the new mix. Listen to each instrument in the mix for level, effects, equalization, limiting, and overall differences. If you hear any inconsistencies between the original and the re-mix, go back to your setup sheet and trace the signal path.

FINAL ASSEMBLY

All final mixes must be tight leadered, timed, and assembled on master reels. Ask about song order and how much time they want between songs. Song order is always a discussion toward the end of a project. Most artists try various combinations of song orders before deciding on which works best. They put a lot of effort into finding a favorable flow of emotion from the start of the recording to the end. Some artists prefer a favorable flow of money, and simply put the best songs first. Once these details are established, and the final assembly is complete, make safety masters of all master mix reels as described in Chapter Nine. After making the safety masters, listen back one last time from beginning to end to check for any dropouts.

LABELLING THE FINAL MIX REEL

Write the individual song titles, times, and the total playing time on the master mix tape label. Of course, all songs must be edited and tight leadered before the total playing time is established. Master tapes that leave the studio should always have typed labels, with all the applicable information as described in Chapter Eight. Most tapes for a commercially released project will be sent or taken to the mastering lab. Note that fast-forwarding a tape may cause uneven packing, so it's best to slow wind the final mixes and let them pack properly for the mastering engineer, then he will do the same for long-term storage of the tapes.

MASTERING

Mastering is the process of final equalization and level matching, done to make each song consistent with the other songs. Sometimes different songs within a project are mixed with different overall equalization. For example, the mix of one song might have more low end than another, or may be printed hotter to tape than the rest. The mastering engineer hears this, and adjusts them so all mixes sound consistent.

If possible, volunteer to take the final mixes to the mastering lab. This is an exceptional place for an eager assistant to really use his ears and hear what the mastering engineer is listening for. By now you should know how the mixes sound, so watch and listen to what the mastering engineer does. This book is not the forum for mastering.

. . . .

Summary

Chapter Eleven explained what is expected of the assistant during mixdown:

• Setting up the control room, the console and the outboard equipment to the engineer's satisfaction.

• Running all mix machines.

• Keeping all paperwork organized throughout the mix, including detailed tape labels, and complete setup sheets for a re-mix.

• Helping print and edit the mixes. Making everyone a copy. Mastering.

CHAPTER TWELVE

. . . .

After the Session

The session ends when everything has been recorded, time has run out, everyone is too weary to continue, or technical problems force the session to stop. Contrary to popular belief, the session does not end when the assistant engineer decides he is tired.

Before everyone leaves, they will agree to the start time for the next session, and what instrument and song to start with. When the session is locked out, start times may change from day to day. When the session is over, everyone gathers their belongings and prepares to leave, but there is still work for the assistant engineer.

THE CLIENT

WORK ORDER

The work order is the daily contract between the client and the recording studio and includes the session events and costs. The producer agrees to the charges incurred by signing the daily work order. The work order is then handed in to the studio manager, who in turn, bills the client. Every studio uses work orders differently, so there is no established standard way to complete them.

SONG TITLE / WORK DONE		INVOICE #	
(AEH)			
	Mixed "Weiner Water Soup Blues"		

	STUDIO A ☐	STUDIO B ☒	COPY ROOM ☐

DATE *August 3*	CLIENT *Black ink Publishing*	P.O. #
TIME BOOKED	ADDRESS	
IN *11am* OUT *2:30 am*		ATTN
TIME USED *15.5 hrs*	ARTIST/SESSION *TUFF BEANS*	PRODUCER *Bob Loblaw*
IN OUT	ENGINEER *Casey Jones*	ASS.ENG. *A. Reader*
FORMAT *Hard drive* ANALOG ☐	DIGITAL ☒	

CONTROL ROOM				TOTALS	RENTALS AND MISC.	
LOCKOUT		DAYS @ $	/DY			
RECORD		HOURS @ $	/HR		*Rented 3 Equalizers*	
OVERDUB		HOURS @ $	/HR		*@$50 = $150*	
MIX	*15.5*	HOURS @ $ *$50*	/HR	*$775*		
COPY		HOURS @ $	/HR			
TRANSFER		HOURS @ $	/HR		TOTAL	*$775*
COPY ROOM					STATE/PROV. TAX	*$54.25*
EDIT		HOURS @ $	/HR		RENTAL	*$150*
LEADER		HOURS @ $	/HR		ADDL.	
COPY		HOURS @ $	/HR		SUB TOTAL	*$979.25*
STOCK					PREV. BAL.	
ANALOG		@ $	/EACH		AMOUNT PAID	*$979.25*
DIGITAL		@ $	/EACH		TOTAL OWED	*$00.00*
DVD		@ $	/EACH		CLIENT APPROVAL	
CD		@ $	/EACH			
ADDITIONAL		@ $	/EACH		ENGINEER APPROVAL	
			TOTAL			

Figure 12.1 *Work Order*

Figure 12.1 is an example of a work order. However the work order is designed, it should always include—

- The name of the person or company paying the studio bill.

- The names of the artist or band, producer, engineer, assistant engineer and which studio was used.

- The date and start time of the session.

- Session events. Studios use different rates for setup, recording, over-dubbing, editing and mixing. Include hours used and any session down time.

- General details of the session, with the names of songs and instruments recorded. Whoever pays the bill will want a daily breakdown, not simply the number of hours used.

- Number of tapes, CDs, DVDs, or any other recording media used, with their appropriate control numbers. (See later in this chapter for more on control numbers.)

- Additional rentals, such as microphones or outboard equipment.

- Any additional charges, such as food or taxicabs.

- Signatures. The producer and/or engineer must sign the work order after every session. Sometimes, if the studio is booked out for a long project, days may go by without getting the work order signed. When the producer finally goes to sign them all, he invariably questions the hours or equipment indicated. With the work order signed after every session, any discrepancies of charges or hours used can be discussed while still fresh in everyone's mind.

- The next session's start time, plus any other information you feel the manager might need, such as any technical problems.

PAYMENT

The studio sends the bill to the money people—the record company, the ad agency, the jingle house or the financial backers. The financial, or billing section of the work order is usually completed by the studio manager. If the client is paying after the session, and the manager is not there, you will have to deal with the payment.

Follow these steps:

1) Work out all the details and costs for the session, and fill in the work order completely. Of course, you will need to know the individual costs of everything, such as the studio rates, discs, batteries, etc. If you don't know these costs, look for an itemized list somewhere on the premises.

2) Get the full payment from the client, then give him the receipt and a copy of the work order—not the other way around.

3) Stash the payment, whether check or cash, in a safe place, such as in the manager's desk, or in the studio safe. Studio policy dictates.

4) If there are any discrepancies regarding costs, call the studio manager. Don't get into discussions with the client over misunderstandings on the work order. Better to telephone the studio manager at 2 a.m. and straighten everything out before the client leaves with the tapes, than hunt the client down the next day to get more money. Red tape and audio tape simply don't mix.

5) Sometimes when the client is working directly off of his own hard drive, there is no choice but to let him take his hard drive with all the songs on it at the end of the session. If the client owes money, these things should be straightened out with management well before the session begins.

SESSION BREAKDOWN

After the work order is signed, and everyone else has left, you can begin the studio breakdown. With a runner helping, the job will be much easier. If you are completing the last session of the day, you should be able to take your time while breaking down.

If there is another session scheduled right after yours, break down the control room first, so the engineer for the next session can get started. It might be helpful to the assistant on the next session to leave anything he needs set up, such as specific microphones, headphones or baffles.

Before starting the breakdown, check again that everything is properly documented. Depending on the session, you may have to write down the settings of equipment in the control room and the studio.

LABELLING AND FILE ORGANIZATION

Once again, proper labelling in the digital realm is essential. Due to the ease of creating new tracks, endless comps, clones of tracks, DAW mixes, slaves, masters, feeders, and copies, each needs a label. Sample rates, sync. sources, formats etc. all need reliable and consistent documentation. Make it your mission to understand and complete all the labelling and naming of every digital file and folder, throughout the project.

DISC STORAGE

In your three-ring binder, store safety disc's of mixes, sessions and songs. Safeties are easy to create and slip into an envelope. Some felt pens can damage discs, so it's better to write any pertinent information on the inner plastic circle, avoiding the actual data area.

TAPES

Remove any tapes from the machines, and place them in their proper boxes. Scan the control room for any applicable paperwork, such as tracksheets and put them with the tapes. Don't leave tapes loaded on a multitrack machine overnight. When a tape must remain loaded overnight, loosen the tape tension from the capstan path to ease pressure on the springs and to relax the relays. Eject any digital multitrack cassettes.

For hard drives, make a DVD copy of the raw tracks as a safety copy. Common practice is to return all recording media to the vault after the session. Insurance policies in most studios dictate that all tapes and recording media not in active use must be safely stored in a cool dry room. If all these are in the control room and anything happens, such as a flood, they might not be covered by insurance. They would, however, be covered with water.

VAULT/CONTROL NUMBERS

In big studios, tapes, discs and hard drives of many different formats come and go on a regular basis, and all should be stored in the vault. The vault, or tape library, is where all the recording media is stored. Never take any unauthorized person into the vault.

No matter how large or small, the vault must be organized in a way to keep track of everything. All incoming and outgoing reels, past, present, and future projects, virgin reels and tapes of different formats must be organized and numbered. With a large vault, a reliable system is needed.

The Dewey Decimal System, named after that wacky librarian Melvil Dewey, is a numbering system used to organize many similar items with different and varied categories. With this system, all non-virgin tapes are given a control number, and can be continually updated within a project.

For example, if the project is numbered 631, multitrack tapes are numbered 631.1.1., 631.1.2.. 631.1.3... while ½" tapes are numbered 631.2.1., 631.2.2... Virgin tapes aren't given control numbers until they are used, or assigned to a project.

MEDIA CONTROL

Because of the wide range of set-up and applications in today's recording, the Nashville Chapter of the Audio Engineering Society (AES) and the National Academy of Recording Arts and Sciences (NARAS) created media control forms similar to the one shown in Figure 12.2.

A media control form should accompany all Masters and Safety Master discs or hard drives on the project. This form contains the date, all the artist information, bit depth, sample rate, file formats, plus the host computer, software and version. As well, in this instance, the plug-ins and number of active and inactive voices are noted. See how additional files, such as notes and lyrics are also included.

OUTGOING MEDIA

Gather all the paperwork—the media control forms, the tracksheets, takesheets, recording maps, all set-up sheets, notes, lyrics, charts and, as the AES says—all data pertinent to the recording project. If the session is going to another studio, the assistant will thank you. If it is going to a record label or music company, then remember, they love organization and lots of paperwork. If you want a record company to keep using your studio, feed them lots of paperwork.

Master tapes and drives always stay at the studio until the bill is fully paid, or an arrangement has been made with the studio manager. If the client is a regular at the studio, he may have a small degree of leeway, but unless

Plug-ins/Peripherals Used

Name	Version	Name	Version	Name	Version

SSL 4000 Plug-ins

Neve compressor plug-ins V7.4.1

Artist *Tuff Beans*   Project#   *631* Disc   of   *1*   *1*

Project/Song   *Too Tuff To Tame*   Date: *August 5, Year*

Label *Crapitol Records* Contact ___ Phone ( )

Producer *Bob Loblaw*   Phone ( )

Studio/Contact *Studio Manager*   Phone ( )

Engineer *Casey Jones*   Phone ( )

Asst. Engineer *A. Reader*   Phone ( )

DAW Platform [X] Mac [ ] PC [ ] Other   DAW Program *Pro-tools*

Host Computer ___   Host Computer OS *Jupitor*   Software Version *16.2*

Bit Depth [ ] 16 [X] 24 Other ___

Sample Rate [ ] 44.1 [ ] 88.2 [ ] 192 [X] 48 [ ] 96 [ ] Other ___

Time Code [ ] 30 [X] 29.97 NDF [ ] 24 [ ] 25 [ ] 29.97 DF [ ] 29.97 DF

[ ] SMPTE Sync Ref [ ] EBU [ ] MTC

File Format [ ] BWAV [ ] AIFF [X] WAV [ ] MP3 [ ] OTHER ___

Songs/Files/Plug-ins

24 active voices, 4 inactive voices

Lyrics and notes
Active tracks
Work tracks
Files and fades for final mix of "Too Tuff..."

Figure 12.2 *Media Control Form*

you have specific authorization, never release anything to anyone, including the musicians. Possession of the masters might be the studio's only real guarantee that the client will pay his outstanding debt. If the studio has no collateral to hold until full payment, there is little that the studio can do when the client doesn't live up to his financial obligations.

TRANSPORTING TAPES/MEDIA

Recording media must often be sent out, either up the street, across town, across the country or around the world. When masters are going away from the studio, safety masters must be made. Safety masters aren't needed if a project has already been released. In other words, if the product is already in the stores or available on-line, don't make the safeties.

Confirm that all the tracksheets, media control forms and tape labels are legible and correct. Write a note telling the assistant who receives the shipment to telephone you if there are any questions about the project.

Load everything into a solid box, wrap it up in heavy paper then clearly mark the destination. If the package is going across town then a runner from either your studio or the other studio will probably deliver them. If the package is going out of town, the value warrants using a reliable courier service. Mailing may not be not the best way to send tapes, no matter how well insured.

Most studios have a standard one or two line form that states who is taking this package, and on what date. The person receiving it signs these forms. The contents being signed for are the result of countless hours of work, and are a serious financial investment. While the studio is usually only responsible for the raw costs if any music is lost or stolen, the damage comes in reputation. A studio that loses songs won't get many recommendations from unsatisfied customers.

CONTROL ROOM

Once the recording media has been dealt with, continue with the break-down of the rest of the control room:

- Confirm that all console and outboard settings are correctly documented, either by computer or by the age old method of writing the settings down on paper. If applicable, make safety backups containing all information before breaking down the console.

- Sometimes certain channels on the console must be left as they are. If so, ask the assistant on the next session if it is possible not to use those channels. When your session returns the next day, the channels still retain their original settings.

- Zero the rest of the console and the outboard equipment. Remove all cords from the patchbay, and clean all pencil marks and remove any adhesive tape.

- Store any samples or computer information in its proper storage format, which may be analog tape, digital tape, or a non-volatile storage device.

- Clean up any ashtrays, empty soda cans, coffee cups, and other trash. If someone from the session accidentally leaves something behind, mark the items with the owner's name and keep them with the daily log.

- If there are any technical problems or pertinent information regarding anything in the studio that may affect the session after yours, leave a note for the next person.

- Again, when the sessions are locked out everything usually stays the same for the next day's recording. If the setup is left overnight, write down the sounds that are still in use, such as an unfinished overdub, in case something gets changed after everyone has left. Invisible studio gremlins have been known to materialize in the gloom of night and mischievously change a favorite setting. For some reason, things may not sound exactly the same the next day.

- Leave a "Do Not Touch" sign for the cleaning staff or anyone else who may enter the studio. You can even run a long strip of adhesive tape from one corner of the console to the other, and again the other way, creating a large ominous X over the console.

- Finally, if it is studio policy, turn off all the equipment, starting with the amplifiers. Then turn off the tape machines, the television, and everything else in the control room, as per studio procedure. If there are keyboards or computers left on, check before switching them off. Massive amounts of important information can be lost with an innocent flick of the "off" switch.

- Collect all the lyrics, sheet music and any other paperwork left behind. Never leave lyrics behind for the people in the next session to throw away, read, or worse, use on their project. If someone in the session writes or draws something brilliant and leaves it behind, save it in a safe place so it won't get thrown out.

STUDIO

Check with the engineer before breaking down the studio, as he will sometimes want certain instruments to stay set up. Setups are sometimes left unchanged and the next session works around them. For example, if the next session is a mixdown session, and your session is returning tomorrow to continue overdubs, the studio is left as is.

Start with the cables. If you start with the microphones, once you move them, the sounds are gone. If you start with the cables, the client still has a little time to mull over the latest recording. If he listens to the song with the new overdub a few times while you are breaking down the cables, and decides he isn't happy with a certain track, it can be re-recorded. As the microphones will still be up, the sound will still be there after simply plugging the cables back into the input panel.

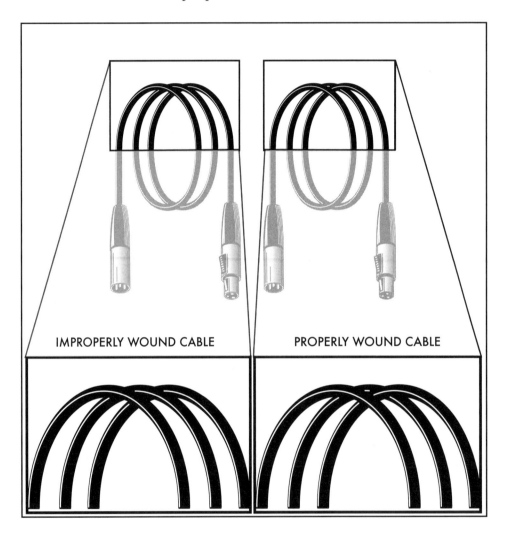

IMPROPERLY WOUND CABLE

PROPERLY WOUND CABLE

Figure 12.3 Winding a Cable

CABLES

Due to the manufacturing process, cables have a natural coil when wound. If you wrap the cable under your arm, like so much rope, it winds in only one direction. When it is unwound, it does so only in one direction, causing it to coil up like a garden hose. The correct way is to wrap it up in an inward-outward motion, so it is wound and unwound the same way with no looping in one direction, and no tangles. Figure 12.3 shows how to properly wrap an XLR cable.

1) Grasp the female, or microphone end in one hand, leaving a bit dangling. With the other hand, grasp the cable and wind one loop over your first hand. The length of the loop should be about the distance from your hand to your elbow.

2) Then with your other hand, grasp the longer part of the cable about three feet (one meter) down.

3) Twist the wrist outward, creating an opposing loop with the long end of the cable.

4) Place this loop in hand one. Go back to step 1 winding the next loop inward. This repeats the inward-outward looping of a cable until it is completely wound.

When the cable is fully wound, you have the male jack at the end of the wound cable. If you always plug the cable in at the microphone input panel first, then unravel as you walk to the microphone stand, the cable will unwind with the same inward-outward direction with no tangles. Excess cable will be left at the stand, in case the microphone needs to be moved.

Warning: Don't plug in a cable, then toss the remaining cable toward the microphone stand, unraveling as it goes. If tossed and unraveled incorrectly, the so-called "tosser" will get a cable full of knots.

After wrapping the cable, connect both ends to each other. Some studios tie a knot with one end of the cable to keep it together, but this is hard on the cable. Hold the cable together with a proper cable tie. Don't use masking tape, as it tears easily, and leaves a sticky residue.

Return the correctly wound cables back to the correct spot in the cable room, as you may be the one who uses the cables next time.

MICROPHONES

Breakdown of microphones occurs throughout the session, not just at the end of it. The assistant may need to set up for another recording situation during the session. Breaking down microphones is the same as setting them up, only reversed:

- Remove the microphones from the stands. Put the microphones away two at a time with one in each hand.

- Some studios leave the microphones on the stands with the XLR cable. When you need one, you just grab the complete setup.

- Count the microphones as you put them away. Unfortunately, smaller pieces of expensive equipment may sometimes "accidentally" drop into someone's pocket. Counting equipment after every session is simply good business practice.

Healthy microphones are the basic building blocks of a good recording studio and when they are well maintained, they should remain in top condition for years.

HEADPHONES, TUNERS, EFFECTS BOXES, DIRECT BOXES

After all the microphones and cables are put away, collect all the headphones. Then collect the smaller items, like headphone boxes, direct boxes, tuners, and put them away. Separate the studio items from the musicians' items, and don't let any musicians leave without all their equipment. All studio items should be clearly marked with the studio's name.

INSTRUMENTS

After all the smaller items are put away, the larger items, such as the drums, amplifiers, and any other musical instruments must be dealt with. Studio musical equipment must be put away, even if it is into the corner. Usually though, the musicians will break down and take their instruments with them.

THE REST OF THE ROOM

- Finally, straighten up all boom stands, and return microphone stands to their proper home. Remove any adhesive tape that may have been put on a stand or on the floor during the session.

- Roll the baffles to their proper storage spot. Keep in mind that rolling a baffle over a stray cable is a great way to slice the cable in half.

- Stack the chairs in a corner.

- Roll up all carpets and rugs and put them in their proper places.

- Take any faulty equipment to the shop, along with a maintenance form explaining the problem.

- After cleaning up all the large items, sweep the floor and organize the studio. You are tidying up for the next assistant, so if he finds it messy, chances are, you'll find it that way after his session. The studio should now be as clean as it can be, and ready for the next session.

THE NEXT SESSION

When there is no session in after you, such as late at night, you may be responsible for locking up the studio. Check that everything in the control room is off, that all tapes and recording media are put away, and all paperwork is complete and where it's supposed to be. Turn off the air conditioner, fans, heaters, photocopy machine, computers, printers, and especially the coffee machine. Turn out all the lights, shut all the doors, and lock all the windows. When all this is done, you can set the burglar alarm, close up shop, and stagger home. But will you?

Everything has been cleaned and ready for tomorrow's first session. It's quarter to three and there's no one here but you and me. Let's sit at the console and discuss an important issue.

LEARNING, THE OLD FASHIONED WAY

After the clients, the producer and the engineer leave, you and the late night staff (often only a runner or two) might be the only ones there. Some over eager assistants may stay and experiment. You aren't supposed to do this, but how else does one really learn to engineer.

If you stay late after a session, or even sneak into the studio at 3 a.m. and start experimenting with the console and outboard equipment, what is the worst thing that can happen? Chances are, if you get caught, you will be reprimanded. So tell the truth. The engineer you work with was using a certain piece of equipment in a way that you didn't understand. To do your job effectively, you must know the complete workings of each piece of equipment, so you stayed late, on your own time, to investigate.

An eager assistant, armed with the vast amounts of information enclosed in this handbook, will be such a great asset to any studio that employs him, that he will be too valuable to be fired. The benefit gained from experimenting is immeasurable. The only way to learn it is to do it. Sometimes, it's better to ask for forgiveness than for permission. Here are a few thoughts on the subject:

- Don't use the client's project, or any song from any important session unless you are authorized. If you erase, delete, lose, or damage anything, the studio will be rightfully held responsible, and you could easily lose your job. Find an old unclaimed or house session.

- Don't bring in your band and record your own songs. If you get caught working on your project, this will be viewed as taking advantage of the studio for your own musical career. The main objective here is to learn the equipment by engineering, not becoming a rock star at the studio's expense. Mind you, it did work for Jon Bon Jovi. The songs you work on should be secondary to the learning process.

- Don't bring in your friends after hours to let them hear the project you are working on. Sure, it's great to impress the babes, but it gets you fired.

ENGINEERING

The term recording engineer refers to the person who gets the sounds. He chooses the microphones, the microphone placement and setup, the outboard, the equalization, and the track layout of all instruments. But simply understanding signal flow and recording techniques is not all it takes to be a good recording engineer. He also must be able to effectively deal with, and get the best out of, sometimes temperamental and egotistical musicians. He must be diplomatic in resolving disputes, and he must be easygoing enough to not get frustrated when things aren't going smoothly. He also has to know how to drink lots of coffee and wear loud Hawaiian shirts.

THE LADDER

The primary goal of the assistant engineer is to move up the recording studio ladder. The fastest way to do this is to think like an engineer, and take over the session. If you are always right there on top of everything, keeping up with the engineer, continually watching and helping, the client will notice this. Soon the producer may not want to spend the extra money hiring a big gun engineer, when he knows that you are available, competent, eager, and most importantly, cheap. Producers are always looking for eager young engineers who know their way around a studio. But remember, if they let you engineer, they let other assistants engineer.

Some engineers may be intimidated by a good assistant who reads all the manuals and books, understands all the equipment, and makes very few mistakes. However, most engineers are happy to help an aspiring assistant.

As recording engineers become producers, assistants become engineers. If you are on the ball, get on well with people, and do a good job, you may get one of these jobs. When you are called on to engineer, remember two things: do everything right, and do everything fast. You may be the best assistant in town, but sitting in the driver's seat and doing the engineering is a whole new ball game.

THE BIG BREAK

Many assistants get their first big break when the main engineer has to leave a session early, or fails to show up at all. This usually leaves the assistant to engineer the session. Studios sometimes rent out cheap time during off hours for lower budget projects, such as demos and house projects. The rate given for the cheaper projects usually includes an engineer. An assistant is given the engineering job because he doesn't charge a lot, and really wants to do it.

However, this is not a job where one good break moves you from assistant to engineer. Usually you work hard as an assistant, then you gradually make the transition. One day you wake and realize "Hey, I'm engineering full time now." Either that or you realize "Hey, I'm unemployed full time now."

Hopefully, toward the end of a project, time restrictions may require another engineer to complete the overdubs. While the main engineer starts mixing, the trusted assistant is occasionally used to engineer some of the overdubs. This usually only happens if the premises has multiple studios.

RECORD CREDITS AND YOU

Credits are amazingly good for getting work as an engineer. If you do any engineering at all on a project, talk to the producer about an "Engineering" or even "Additional Engineering" credit. Although credits are important for your career as an engineer, the guidelines for credits are vague. There will be times when you work on a project for a great length of time, yet not see your name on a final release. On the other hand, you may work on a project for a day, and get a great credit.

- An "Engineer" credit is better than an "Assistant Engineer" credit.

- An "Assistant Engineer" credit is better than being in the "Thank You" column.

- Anything is better than being in the "This Idiot Erased The Vocal Track" column.

STAY IN CONTACT

Establish and maintain contacts with key producers and engineers. They deal with assistant engineers all the time, so show them that you want to be remembered, maybe even hired as an engineer in the future.

FINAL WORDS

Well that's it. I hope you get as much pleasure out of reading this book as I did writing it. Working in a recording studio can be rewarding and fun. I sincerely wish you luck in your chosen career.

. . . .

Summary

Chapter Twelve explained what is expected of the assistant engineer after the session ends:

- Dealing with the client after the session, including filling in the work order, and receiving payment.

- Putting all tapes and hard drives away and, if the client is taking tapes, filling in the tape control forms.

- Breaking down the control room and studio after the session.

- Working your way up to engineer.

Date

Artist

DIGITAL REEL LABEL

Artist _____   Date _____

Producer _____   Client _____

Engineer _____   Studio   ☐ A ☐ B ☐ C

Assistant _____   Reel _____ of _____

DIGITAL MACHINE INFORMATION

Digital Machine _____   Tracks _____   Tape Speed _____

Bit Depth	☐ 16		Sample Rate	☐ 44.1 ☐ 88.2 ☐ 192
	☐ 24 Other _____			☐ 48 ☐ 96 ☐ _____

Time Code Format	☐ 30	☐ 29.97 NDF	☐ 24	☐ SMPTE Sync Ref (For master)
				☐ EBU
	☐ 25	☐ 29.97 DF		☐ MTC

TITLES	TAKE	LOCATE	COMMENTS

Titles

Reel
___
of
___

Library

TAKESHEET / RECORDING MAP

Title: _____   Date _____

Artist _____   Client _____

Producer _____   Studio   ☐ A ☐ B ☐ C

Engineer _____   Assistant _____

TITLES	TAKE	LOCATE	COMMENTS

| FS - FALSE START | CT - COMPLETE TAKE | INC - INCOMPLETE TAKE | CH - CHOICE |

Tracksheet

	TITLE:
	ARTIST:
	PRODUCER:
	ENGINEER:
	CLIENT:

☐ 48 TK ☐ 32 TK ☐ 24 TK ☐ 16 TK ☐ 8 TK

1		2		3		4	
DATE:	MIC:	DATE:	MIC:	DATE:	MIC:	DATE:	MIC:
ENG:	STUDIO:	ENG:	STUDIO:	ENG:	STUDIO:	ENG:	STUDIO:
9		10		11		12	
DATE:	MIC:	DATE:	MIC:	DATE:	MIC:	DATE:	MIC:
ENG:	STUDIO:	ENG:	STUDIO:	ENG:	STUDIO:	ENG:	STUDIO:
17		18		19		20	
DATE:	MIC:	DATE:	MIC:	DATE:	MIC:	DATE:	MIC:
ENG:	STUDIO:	ENG:	STUDIO:	ENG:	STUDIO:	ENG:	STUDIO:

DATE:		TAPE:		SPEED: ☐ 30 IPS ☐ 15 IPS ☐ DIGITAL

STUDIO: ☐ A ☐ B ☐ C   **N. R.:** ☐ DOLBY ☐ DBX ☐ _____

REEL: **OF:**   **SAMPLING RATE:** ☐ 48 K ☐ 44.1 K

TONES ON REEL_____ ☐ HEAD ☐ TAIL   **BIT DEPTH** ☐ 16 ☐ 24 ☐ OTHER

ASSISTANT ENGINEER:

☐ 4 TK | ☐ MASTER   ☐ SAFETY   ☐ SLAVE   ☐ CLONE

5	6	7	8
DATE: MIC:	DATE: MIC:	DATE: MIC:	DATE: MIC:
ENG: STUDIO:	ENG: STUDIO:	ENG: STUDIO:	ENG: STUDIO:
13	14	15	16
DATE: MIC:	DATE: MIC:	DATE: MIC:	DATE: MIC:
ENG: STUDIO:	ENG: STUDIO:	ENG: STUDIO:	ENG: STUDIO:
21	22	23	24
DATE: MIC:	DATE: MIC:	DATE: MIC:	DATE: MIC:
ENG: STUDIO:	ENG: STUDIO:	ENG: STUDIO:	ENG: STUDIO:

DAW TRACKSHEET / RECORDING MAP

Title _____ Date _____

Artist _____ Client _____

Producer _____ Studio ☐ A ☐ B ☐ C

Engineer _____ Assistant _____

DAW INFORMATION

DAW Platform   ☐ Mac ☐ PC ☐ Other   DAW Program _____

Host Computer _____ Host Computer OS _____ Software Version _____

| Bit Depth ☐ 16 ☐ 24 Other_____ | Sample Rate ☐ 44.1 ☐ 88.2 ☐ 192 ☐ 48 ☐ 96 ☐ Other____ |

Time Code Format ☐ 30 ☐ 29.97 NDF ☐ 24   ☐ SMPTE   Sync Ref (For master)
                  ☐ 25 ☐ 29.97 DF   ☐ EBU
                                              ☐ MTC

File Format ☐ BWAV ☐ AIFF ☐ WAV ☐ MP3 ☐ OTHER _____

Sync Source _____ Hard Disc _____ Notes _____

Plug ins _____

General Tracking Notes
_____
_____
_____
_____

MAINTENANCE REPORT NO.

SESSION _____ DATE _____

ENGINEER _____ TIME _____

ASSISTANT _____ STUDIO   A ☐   B ☐   C ☐

SYMPTOMS PLEASE BE EXPLICIT - INCLUDE ENVIRONMENT OF PROBLEM

TEMPORARY ACTION TAKEN:

REPAIRED BY: _____ DATE _____

DIAGNOSIS:

PARTS SENT OR ORDERED: _____ DATE: _____

PARTS RECEIVED: _____ DATE: _____

Artist _____ Project# _____

Song _____ Date _____

Label _____ Contact _____ Phone ( ) _____

Producer _____ Phone ( ) _____

Engineer _____ Phone ( ) _____

Assistant Engineer _____ Phone ( ) _____

ANALOG MACHINE INFORMATION

Analog Tape Machine(s) _____ Tracks _____ Tape Speed _____

Tones _____ Ref. Level 0VU = _____ Noise Reduction _____

Time Code Format	☐ 30	☐ 29.97 NDF	☐ 24	☐ SMPTE	Sync Ref (For master)
				☐ EBU	
	☐ 25	☐ 29.97 DF		☐ MTC	

DIGITAL MACHINE INFORMATION

Digital Machine _____ Tracks _____ Tape Speed _____

| Bit Depth | ☐ 16 | | Sample Rate | ☐ 44.1 ☐ 88.2 ☐ 192 |
| | ☐ 24 Other _____ | | | ☐ 48 ☐ 96 ☐ Other _____ |

Time Code Format	☐ 30	☐ 29.97 NDF	☐ 24	☐ SMPTE	Sync Ref (For master)
				☐ EBU	
	☐ 25	☐ 29.97 DF		☐ MTC	

DAW INFORMATION

DAW Platform ☐ Mac ☐ PC ☐ Other   DAW Program _____

Host Computer _____ Host Computer OS _____ Software Version _____

| Bit Depth | ☐ 16 | | Sample Rate | ☐ 44.1 ☐ 88.2 ☐ 192 |
| | ☐ 24 Other _____ | | | ☐ 48 ☐ 96 ☐ Other _____ |

Time Code Format	☐ 30	☐ 29.97 NDF	☐ 24	☐ SMPTE	Sync Ref (For master)
				☐ EBU	
	☐ 25	☐ 29.97 DF		☐ MTC	

File Format ☐ BWAV ☐ AIFF ☐ WAV ☐ MP3 ☐ OTHER _____

Sync Source _____ Hard Disc _____ Notes _____

Plug ins _____

_____

_____

ARTIST _____ DATE _____

PRODUCER _____ STUDIO A ☐ B ☐ C ☐

ENGINEER _____ ASSISTANT _____

INSTRUMENT	MICROPHONE	PARAMETER	INPUT	BUSS	OUTBOARD

Notes

Name	Version	Name	Version

Plug-ins/Peripherals Used

Artist	Project#	Disc of
Project/Song		Date:
Label	Contact	Phone ( )
Producer		Phone ( )
Studio/Contact		Phone ( )
Engineer		Phone ( )
Asst. Engineer		Phone ( )

DAW Platform ☐ Mac ☐ PC ☐ Other DAW Program ____________

Host Computer ________ Host Computer OS ________ Software Version ________

Bit Depth ☐ 16 ☐ 24 Other ______

Sample Rate ☐ 44.1 ☐ 88.2 ☐ 192 ☐ 48 ☐ 96 ☐ Other ______

Time Code ☐ 30 ☐ 29.97 NDF ☐ 24 ☐ 25 ☐ 29.97 DF ☐ 29.97 DF

Sync Ref ☐ SMPTE ☐ EBU ☐ MTC

File Format ☐ BWAV ☐ AIFF ☐ WAV ☐ MP3 ☐ OTHER ____________

Songs/Files/Plug-ins

AEH	SONG TITLE / WORK DONE		INVOICE #	
	STUDIO A ☐	STUDIO B ☐	COPY ROOM ☐	
DATE	CLIENT		P.O. #	
TIME BOOKED	ADDRESS			
IN OUT			ATTN	
TIME USED	ARTIST/SESSION		PRODUCER	
IN OUT	ENGINEER		ASS.ENG.	
FORMAT	ANALOG ☐	DIGITAL ☒		

CONTROL ROOM			TOTALS	RENTALS AND MISC.	
LOCKOUT	DAYS @ $	/DY			
RECORD	HOURS @ $	/HR			
OVERDUB	HOURS @ $	/HR			
MIX	HOURS @ $	/HR			
COPY	HOURS @ $	/HR			
TRANSFER	HOURS @ $	/HR		TOTAL	
COPY ROOM				STATE/PROV. TAX	
EDIT	HOURS @ $	/HR		RENTAL	
LEADER	HOURS @ $	/HR		ADDL.	
COPY	HOURS @ $	/HR		SUB TOTAL	
STOCK				PREV. BAL.	
ANALOG	@ $	/EACH		AMOUNT PAID	
DIGITAL	@ $	/EACH		TOTAL OWED	
DVD	@ $	/EACH		CLIENT APPROVAL	
CD	@ $	/EACH			
ADDITIONAL	@ $	/EACH		ENGINEER APPROVAL	
		TOTAL			

	INVENTORY						
AEH	SESSION _____						
	ENGINEER _____			CLIENT _____			
	ASSISTANT _____			STUDIO A ☐ B ☐ C ☐			

Date	Multitrack	CD	DVD	BLU-RAY	$1/2''$ Analog	DAT	Additional

PLEASE INCLUDE INVENTORY USED ON YOUR DAILY WORK ORDER.

A

A-DAT 185
AC Cables 21
After Basic Tracks 169
Alexander Graham Bell 43
Alignments 84
Analog 1/4" 76
Analog Mix Machine 208
Analog Tape Machines 81
Apprentice 4
Assembly Edits 170
Assistant Engineer 16
Attitude 8
Auto-input 92 120
Auto Region Fade In/out 171
Aux. Sends 79
Azimuth 84

B

Baffles 35
Balanced Cables 47
Bass Amplifier 31
Batteries 23
Bi-directional 64
Bias 91
Bit Depth 78
Bob Dylan 33
Bon Jovi 142
Bouncing 197

BPM 212
Breaking Down The Mix 233
Bussing 116

C

Cardioid 64
CD Burner 218
Center Section 110
Changing Cables 147
Changing Headphones 148
Changing Microphones 146
Changing Microphone Parameters 147
Changing Patches 149
Changing Tracks 196
Channel 81
Click Generators 103
Clients 13
Clipping 41 209
Closing The Session 177
Combo Amplifiers 30
Common Mode Rejection 48
Comping 197, 198
Connections And Placement 57
Connection Mounts 66
Console Status Mode 116 188
Console 47 113
Copies 223
Copy Room 224
Credits 255
Cross-normalling 117

Crosspatching 211
Cues 166
Cue Mix 194
Cue Sends 122
Cue Station 72

D

Daily Log 139
DAT Recorders 209 217
DAW 76
DAW Tracksheet 155
dBFS 43
dBu 43
dBv 43
Deadpatch 112
Delay Chart 213
Destination Device 48
Digital Audio Workstation 75
Digital Cassettes 185
Digital Connections 76
Digital Levels 43
Direct Box 51
Direct Input Boxes 54
Disc/DAT Labelling 218
Disc Allocation 201
Disc Storage 241
Distortion Pedals 55
Distortion 41 46
Documenting The Mix 225
Down Time 134
Drums 29
Duct Tape 19
Duties 7
Dynamic Range 43

E

Editing The Mix 219
Edits 170
Edit Reel 221
Edit Window 78
Effects Boxes 55
Environments 20
EOS 207
Exercising 90

F

Feeders 160
File Management 178
File Organization 241
Final Assembly 235
Final Microphone Placement 147
Final Mixes 205
Finding The Song 184

G

Gene Simmons 220
George Martin 14
Grounding 22
Ground Lifter 23
Ground Loop 52
Guide Tracks 199
Guide Vocal 63
Guitar Amplifiers 30

H

Half Normal 112
Harmonics 41
Headphones 70
Headphone Boxes 70

Headroom 42
High Impedance Cable Ext. 60
Hours And Wages 6
House Project 5

I

I/O Section 207
Impedance 47, 50
In-line Microphone Pad 61
Input/setup Sheet 24
Input Levels 215
Input Section 110
Insert Edits 170
Insert Send 189
Instrument Setup Sheets 173
Interference 48
Intern 4
Inventory Sheets 141
Isolation Booths 37

J

Jingles 17 170

K

Keith Richards 7
KISS 142

L

Labelling The Reel 166
Leader Tape 221
Leslie 32
Levels 41, 44
Light Pipe 76
Line Inputs 121

M

Maintenance Forms 137
Mastering 236
Master Multitrack Reels 180
Master Sends And Returns 123
Master Session Folder 76 178
Master Session 78
Master Tape Label 182
Master Trim 117
Media Control Form 244
Media Retrieval 144
Memory Markers 207
Micropascals 43
Microphones 64
Microphone Inputs 120
Microphone Input Panel 52
Microphone Placement 67
Microphone Stands 38
MIDI 49
Mistakes 142
Mixing 203
Mix Setup Sheets 233
Mix Window 78
Monitor Mix 193
Monitor Section 110
Monitor 104
Mult 118
Mute Regions 178

N

Nanowebers/VU 85
Nanowebers Per Meter Squared 85
Noise Floor 42

Non-shielded Cables 49
Normals 111

O

Octave 43
Omni-directional 64
Open Reel Labels 163
Open Reel Recording 80
Open Reel Tracksheet 157
Optimum Operating Level 42
Organs 32
Oscillator 91 209
Outboard Equipment 49 96
Outgoing Media 243
Overload 41

P

Patchbay 118
Patchcords 118
Patching 227
Payment 240
Phantom Power 120
Phase 48
Piano 32
Playback Alignment 86
Playlists 155 171
Plug-ins 76
Polar Patterns 64
Pop Filters 69
Power Amplifiers 23
Power Supply 65
Power Transformers 21
Power 43

Practice Your Edits 223
Pre-amplifier 41
Previous Sound 192
Progress Chart 167
Punching In 194

Q

Quick-lock Connectors 67

R

RCA Cables 49
Re-mix 234
Record-ready 116
Recording Basic Tracks 144 151
Recording Engineers 11
Recording Map 155
Recording Overdubs 184
Record Alignment 90
Record Pad 93
Record Producer 12
Reference Point 43
Regions 171
Rehearse Mode 197
Repairs 172
Résumés 3
Returning Data 201
RF (Radio Frequency) 49
Ring Tones 17
Road Cases 28
Roll-offs 64
Rolling Stones 7
Room Microphones 70
Rough Mixes 204
RTZ (Return To Zero) 216

Runner 4
Running Cables 56
Running The Recorder 152

S

S/PDIF 76
Safety Track 195
Sample Rate 76, 78
Schools 1
Scribble Strip 113
Session Breakdown 241
Session Information 229
Session Priorities 125
Session Sheet 76
Setting Up The Studio 186
Setup Sheet Storage 233
Setup Window 78
Shielded Cables 49
Signal Processing 41
Signal Routing 188
Signal To Noise Ratio 43
Slave Sessions 199
Song Title—Master 178
Sound Effects 17
Sound Envelope 46
Sound Pressure Level 43
Source Device 48
Source Impedance 51
Source 160
Speakers 104
Speaker Cables 49
Speaker Cue Setup 108
Speaker Placement 106
Speaker Ties 53
Spectrum Analyzer 109

Splice 181
Splicing Block 221
Split Amplifier 31
Stereo Cables 47
Studio Managers 15
Supplies 18

T

Takesheet/Recording Map 162
Talkback 123
Tape Edits 220
Tape Label 164
Technical Staff 135
Tech Shop 136
Telephone Protocol 130
Testing The Inputs 190
Tone Reel Tapes 84
TOS 207
Tracksheets 154
Track 81
Transporting Tapes/Media 245
Tuners 33
Tuning Tone 152

U

Unbalanced Cables 48
Undoing A Tape Edit 223

V

Vault/Control Numbers 242
Video 104
Vocal Tuning 199
Voltage 43
Volume Units 42

W

WAV Audio File 76
White Noise 109
Winding A Cable 248
Windscreens 69
Workstation 19
Work Order 238

X

XLR Cables 47

Y

Your Personal Collection 225

Z

Zeroing The Console 246

ASSISTANT ENGINEERS HANDBOOK
SECOND EDITION

Written and Illustrated by Tim Crich

- Over 300 pages, fully illustrated 7" x 10". Perfect bound.
- Packed with proven recording studio secrets.
- Complete setups for basics, overdubs and mixing.
- Proper microphone handling and setup.
- Most efficient ways to complete all paperwork.
- Needed pointers on recording studio itiquette.
- Established procedures to keep the session moving.
- Key priorities for before, during and after the session.
- Essential tips on setup and breakdown of all equipment.
- Required reading in audio schools across America.
- Much, much more.

BLACK INK PUBLISHING - ISBN - 978 0 9698223 3 2

RECORDING TIPS FOR ENGINEERS
SECOND EDITION

Written and illustrated by Tim Crich

- Over 300 pages, fully illustrated 7" x 10". Perfect bound.
- Pesky technical information kept to a minimum.
- Written in simple point form. No endless rambling.
- Established procedures to get the very best recordings.
- Proper microphone choice and final placement.
- Effective equalization and compression methods.
- Key procedures for before, during and after the session.
- Huge Chapter on professional sounding mixes.
- Advance your career as a Recording Engineer.
- Includes easy to understand digital appendix.
- Dial in great sounds from any size recording studio.
- Much, much more.

FOCAL PRESS (IMPRINT OF ELSEVIER) - ISBN - 0 240 51974 4
www.focalpress.com.

ORDER BOTH BOOKS AT www.aehandbook.com